# THE THREE-FOLD MIMESIS OF LIFE

## VOLUME 1

Which of these babies develops into which of these adults most often depends on their developmental process in Stage 1 Mimesis.

## DR. RONALD BARNES

Volume 1 of the Three-Fold Mimesis of Life


Mimesis: Background, Definition, Evolution

And


Developmental Theories of Psychology:
Foundation for Mimesis Construction


*With Aforethought, you can construct your own Mimesis*


Dr. Ronald Barnes

ISBN: 978-1-961677-03-6 (Paperback)
ISBN: 978-1-967375-89-9 (Hardback)
ISBN: 978-1-967375-86-8 (E-book)

Library of Congress Control Number: 2025920490

Printed in the United States of America

Published by:

info@thequippyquill.com
(302) 295-2278

# Table of Contents


Preface .................................................................1

**Introduction** .....................................................3

Chapter 1: **Background on Mimesis** ...............11

The Evolution of Mimesis .......................................17

Three-Fold Mimesis (Paul Riceour's Version).....23

Stages of the Three-Fold Mimesis ........................26

The Relationship between the Three-Fold

Mimesis of Life and Lived Experiences...............28

The Three-Fold Mimesis of an individual's Life is

the Representation of that Individual's evolution,

development and reality ........................................31

The Time Factor of Mimesis ................................35

Chapter 2: **The Foundation of the Mimesis of Life** .....41

The Psychological Foundation of Mimesis

Construction...........................................................41

Life Experiences Influence Mimesis .....................44

Childhood Attachments Affect Adult

Relationships ........................................................49

Psychological Theories of Development that

Influence the Three-Fold Mimesis of Life...........51

Psychology Theories of Development...................53

The Critical Role of Social Referencing...............79

Childhood Validation and Development of Well-Being ....................................................................82

The Environment as a Determinant Factor in Mimesis Construction (Lived Experiences and Choices).....................................................................86

Breaking the Cycle of Dysfunction........................87

**End Note**s .................................................................89

# Preface

This Volume I of the *Three-Fold Mimesis of Life* is dedicated to the fortunate who lead a productive life, to parents around the world who raise their kids to be constructive contributors to society. The author also dedicates this book to those kids who grow into adulthood and may not have experienced proper guidance during their formative years, but overcame negative life experiences and were motivated to achieve a positive, constructive life.

This book is also dedicated to those who are in the midst of their developmental process and encountering challenging life experiences. You are encouraged to stay strong, persevere, and not quit or falter in the face of negativity. The primary purpose of this book is to inform the people of the world, especially the young, that the paths they take in life and the decisions they make define who they are; who they will become, how others will perceive them, and what their legacy will be. Your schema is defined by the decisions you make regarding the phenomena you encounter. The people you associate with give understanding to your schema. Your schema is determined by your behavior.

> **Schema** is a mental structure to help us understand how things work. It has to do with how we organize knowledge. As we take in new information, we connect it to other things we know, believe, or have experienced. And those connections form a sort of structure in the brain. An individual's **schema** gives a definition/description of who they are. Schema is manifested in behavior.

Everyone encounters difficulties and challenges in life. It is how people manage, handle, and resolve life challenges that determine who they are, who they will become, how others respond to them, and what their legacy will be. Aligned with Schema, Mimesis is a representation of an individual's reality. Kids are impulsive. They often live in the moment, giving little thought to the future. With proper socialization, understanding the principles of schema / Mimesis construction, and with guidance, children growing into adolescents and growing into adults can construct their own Mimesis with aforethought.

# **Introduction**

The Three-Fold Mimesis of Life, Volumes I, II, III and IV, is a viewpoint that gives understanding to the relationship and alignments between birth (inception of consciousness), life (Active consciousness, living and accumulating lived experiences, experiencing encountered phenomena, responding to lived experiences and phenomena), and catharsis (the process of releasing strong or pent-up emotions leading to self-realization, a transformational process and a reflective process). Catharsis can also involve the response from the world outside of yourself regarding opinions on how others perceive and evaluate your life. Finally, the culmination of birth, life and catharsis ending with death (the Final Mimesis), the state of non-being or the afterlife; death and the final release from hardships in life and being, relief from anxiety, dispensation of repressed emotions, elimination of pain, suffering and fears. The state of non-being represents the final anecdote with which others remember an individual. The end of life does not have to be a depressing phenomenon. For those who accept the reality of their finitude, and have lived a rewarding life, the end of life can reflect a rewarding and satisfying state of being when the individual reflects on their life with a positive perspective and realizes accomplishment. Do not misinterpret that accepting death, in any way, rivals the welcome acceptance of a prize, a diploma or even accepting news of an illness that is cured. Death is final. However, a positive and healthy constructed Mimesis can give the individual a life full of positive lived experiences that will contribute to mitigating death fear, death anxiety while accepting the end of conscious existence on this world as a phenomenon beyond our control. Death is inevitable. Death is the price people pay for life. The only way not to encounter death is not to be born. While catharsis and reflection can take place throughout an individual's conscious life. Stage 3 is the stage where catharsis and reflection usually takes place in more depth because in the later stage of life the individual has more life experiences upon which to reflect and the emplotment of life experiences gives the individual a complete understanding of their Mimesis and their Mimesis construction. A contributing factor to mitigating the anxiety of the final Mimesis is to begin the process of positive Mimesis construction as early in life as possible and be conscious of every moment we are bless with lifetime.

The phenomena of coming into consciousness or birth; the state of being, life or living and the accumulation of lived experiences; is background for Catharsis; a reflection and response to emplotments[1] that create the narrative of an individual's life and lived experiences.

**The Mimesis of Life is the representation of an individual's reality**. Mimesis conceptualizes whether the individual is a good person, a bad person, a smart person, a criminal, an individual with credibility, and individual not to be believed, an individual to follow/not to follow, an individual to vote for, or an individual to respect, an individual whose company you want to be in or an individual you want to avoid. The Mimesis of Life represents an individual's reality, comprised of self-perception, and including how others perceive the individual. The foundation for the construction of an individual's Mimesis begins at Stage 1. The individual has agency over their Mimesis construction begins at Stage 2, as the individual responds to lived experiences and phenomena they encounter.

---

[1] Emplotments – The assembly of a series of historical events into a narrative with a plot.

> **Reality** is defined as a perspective or things in life that are commonly observed and verified to exist, things that are consistent and not random or influenced by conformity or mass hysteria. Something that is perceived as real and is physically experienced by the senses.

Death, the end of life and cessation of lived experiences; is the final Mimesis, the state of non-being. It is the viewpoint of this author that not only are the states of being and non-being related, they are continuous and contiguous states of human energy that display a transformation of consciousness. The Final Mimesis (death) is considered, by some, to be the end-all. Then again, some people consider the end of life to be a transcendental state of being.[1]  Death is interdependent and dependent on life. One cannot die unless they are born and live, and if you are born and live, you will, without a doubt, experience death. As people age, they normally become more conscious of the end of their life cycle.

The caregiver relationship, education, religion, and lived experiences and individual encounters all become mediators that align and integrate the phenomena of birth, life, the human perspective an individual develops, and death. The mediation is based on the alignment of an individual's lived experiences with the decisions they make. For many people, religion weighs in at almost every stage of human ontology. At birth, when the conscious state of being occurs; with the accumulation of lived experiences; baptism, education, activities, work, church attendance, marriage, and the creation of a family. For many people, religion is prevalent during the accumulation of life experiences and establishes guidelines for behavior, ethics, and morality. Religion connects birth (baptism), life (church attendance, marriage), and death (funeral service) for many individuals. Religion, for those who consider themselves religious, contains insights and guides on how to live and strategically identify and define the lived experiences one will encounter throughout their life. Religious individuals reinforce life guides on a weekly basis through church participation. Some religions reinforce life guides daily by praying multiple times per day. Religion also weighs in during life experience by proposing a cultural worldview that God exists and there is an existence after death. The end-of-life ceremonial process, funeral services, reinforces the concept of religion being a portal to the afterlife. Religion proposes the belief that death is not the end of consciousness. Religion has a role in every aspect of the "Human Being," from inception, during human life, and at the end-of-life experience. Religion introduces, maintains, and reinforces a cultural worldview that supports individuals to select phenomena and engage lived experiences with ethical and moral integrity. Religion provides insights and influences individuals on how to live and how to die; how to accept the inevitable reality, death. Religion, for some, reconciles the anxiety that accompanies the realization that life and living on earth are finite. There are a considerable number of research studies presenting evidence that conclude religious commitment produces a happier, more satisfied life and well-being during an individual's life experiences. Studies also concluded that religious individuals who are involved in religious participation during their life have an inverse relationship with fear of death, dying, death, and death anxiety.[2]

Religion serves a symbiotic relationship with government, despite the notion that church and state are separate. Almost all politicians end their speeches with the phrase, "God Bless the United States of America". Federal, state, and local laws that determine what an individual can and cannot do are, significantly, based in religious doctrine. Boundaries are established, maintained, and enforced to guide human behavior. The difference between the religious behavior constructs and the legal behavior constructs is that legal behavior constructs are accompanied by immediate reinforcement, either positive or negative. Religious behavior constructs have an existential transcendental delayed reinforcement process. Break the law and you will go to jail, now. Sin and you will go to hell when you die. But if you declare belief in God and sincere repentance, your sentence to hell will be commuted, and you will go to heaven. Therefore, the religious constructs do not have the immediate reinforcement and certainty of punishment function characteristic of the legal system. However, ethical, moral, and legal behaviors constructs play a role in directing human behavior and the choices individuals make in their lived experiences they encounter throughout their life. Conversely, some individuals make decisions and choose behaviors characterized by negative lived experiences that result in their life taking a destructive and fatalistic direction.

The developmental process individuals experience is a critical factor in the lived experiences they encounter and the outcome of their Mimesis. Understanding the importance and responsibility of guiding, training, and having influence over the life of a child can determine how the child's life turns out. Theories of development give insight into how the early stages of development influence the life of a person. This book gives a synopsis of the value of a human being's ability to understand and construct their own reality, their Mimesis. It is said that the reality of an individual is based on the individual's perception of who they are, the perception of who others perceive them to be, but the real person is usually a combination of both perceptions.

Reality is reflected in behavior. *Perception* and *reality* can have different meanings. The perception occurs in the mind. Mental gymnastics can turn a belief into reality. Reality exists outside of the mind and is not manipulated. It is displayed behavior. An individual's reality is when both the individual's self-perception align with how others perceive the individual. While perception is not reality, perception can become a person's reality when perception influences behavior and both perception and behavior are aligned.[3] The true, real, and authentic human being will emerge when catharsis occurs. Catharsis is the emotional release that synthesizes and converges the perception one has of themselves with the perception others have of them, and both align with behavior. The development of stability in one's human catharsis crystalizes as the individual has lived experiences reflecting the stability of their Mimesis, their reality.[4] Mimesis is the representation of the individual's reality.

The process of catharsis can occur during an individual's lived experiences. We live in a dynamic world. Things change, people change, situations change, phenomena are dynamic. Contrary to the Hindu belief that people are born into caste, this book presents evidence that the caste system of belief is not valid in Western civilization. Frankly, it is questionable whether the caste system is valid or credible to human existence in Western civilization. The caste system rivals slavery and racism as a means to repress and suppress human beings. The caste system is a social construct whose purpose is to maintain the status quo, to keep others down to perpetuate a repressive system of humanity, while giving privilege to the select few. In that regard, there is a common link between caste and institutionalized racism. The truth is that people born of disadvantage can construct their lives to become fruitful, productive beings who contribute greatness to society. People born into disadvantaged circumstances can rise into greatness. In America, poverty can be a perpetual state of mind and social condition if individuals do not realize they have the ability to break the cycle. Greatness is within the capability of all human beings. Conversely, individuals born into privilege can encounter the misfortune of experiencing dysfunctional circumstances that cause ruination in their lives. Some individuals are fortunate to have good guidance in their early childhood and adolescence, which perpetuates positive lived experiences throughout their lives.

The value of this book is evident because there are so many young people who are losing their lives to dysfunction and literally, to death.

*"Experts say pressures on youth have been amplified over the past decade by internet and social media platforms where bullying and aggressive marketing of hateful ideologies – drugs - and weapons – is rampant".* [5]

Gun violence is rising throughout the United States, higher than in any other country in the civilized world. The United States also has the highest rate of privately owned guns per person in the world. Never in history has gun violence been so rampant, except during wars. The real tragedy is that guns are a catalyst for kids killing kids. Youth violence is more rampant in America than in any other civilized country in the world. Experts place some blame on social media and the unrestricted access to media that supports dysfunction. Individuals who are poor, who are outliers in receiving the benefits of society, can harbor anger that is often displaced and perpetuated toward those in close proximity.  No jobs, no money, poor housing, poor health and health systems, no motivation, poor education, all contribute to the formula for dysfunction.  Some individuals inflict violence out of a perverse desire to make a difference in the world. Others are driven by mental illness. Pandemic isolation, social media, and dysfunctional guidance make an individual subject to have their mind influenced by negative ideologies. Dysfunctional behavior is manifested by a negative influence on an individual's developmental process and exposure to negative phenomena; they succumb. If an individual encounters hardship in their developmental process and does not overcome the hardship, then their potential for experiencing dysfunction in their life increases. If the cycle of dysfunction is not broken, then the individual's propensity for dysfunction, violence, criminality, incarceration, and premature death increases.

Chapter 1

# Background on Mimesis

The concept of mimesis dates to the times of Plato and Aristotle. Originally, mimesis was a critical and philosophical term used with a wide range of meanings: imitation, representation, mimicry, similarity, and the act of resembling. The term mimesis was originally derived from the Greek *mimesis*, meaning to imitate.[6] Mimesis has meaning depending on the act of expression, the presentation, or depending on the context of its use and the manner presented. In ancient Greece, mimesis was a concept permeated throughout the arts. It referenced models of beauty, truth, honesty, and goodness. Mimesis was also a compliment to creativity, a means for humans to be in touch with phenomena, and a means to give animation to concepts or inanimate objects to accent their purpose. For example, in a play where an individual acts as, or mimics a tree, a flower, or other type of inanimate object, is an example of the early use of Mimesis. The term "mimesis" is derived from an ancient Greek term that means imitation of the real.[7]

Plato considered mimesis as "the appearance of the external image of things. In his view, reality was not to be found in the world of the objects but in the realm of the Ideas. Plato viewed Mimesis as an imitation of nature. Plato sees in the arts an occupation that is inferior to science and philosophy, but that is also a potential source of corruption". Plato had an esoteric viewpoint of mimesis. In his theory of Mimesis, Plato says that all art is mimetic by nature; art is an imitation of life. He believed that 'idea' is the ultimate reality. Art imitates idea, and so it is an imitation of reality.[8] Plato took mimesis to be a unifying concept where artistic presentation represented the reality of nature.

One has to consider the social location and values in the era of Plato and Aristotle, during the times of ancient Greece, the positions of Plato and Aristotle as philosophers, as contributors to the social order during their era. During the times of Plato and Aristotle, Mimesis governed the idea of creation of the artistic work in Ancient Greece. For both Plato and Aristotle, mimesis meant the representation of Nature, of the physical world.  The physical world was the model for beauty.[9]

Aristotle also saw Mimesis as a representation of nature and as a concept of imitation. Imitation is one of the distinctive aspects of human nature, and a way for humans to understand the nature of art, the art of expression. According to Aristotle, the process and, one of the purposes of Mimesis is as a learning concept. Aristotle states that, *"The instinct of imitation is implanted in man from childhood, one difference between him and other animals being that he is the most imitative of living creatures, and through imitation learns his earliest lessons; and no less universal is the pleasure felt in things imitated."*[10] When Plato used the word and meaning of mimesis in reference to a narrative description of phenomena, the use of mimesis in concept and meaning shifted to a literary context. Plato and Aristotle viewed Mimesis as depicting realism, naturalism, and authenticity in art, poetry, and literature.

Mimesis, according to Aristotle, is an active aesthetic process. He argues that 'imitation is given us by nature, and men who are endowed with these gifts, gradually develop them and finally create the art of poetry. The poet does not imitate reality but brings reality into existence through 'mimesis'. Both Plato and Aristotle considered Mimesis an artistic and poetic phenomenon.[11] "According to Aristotle, poetry was completely based on philosophical thoughts, while history is based on facts. The historians write about factual reality, whereas the poet anticipates the ultimate truth of life. He believed that poetry is the mother and caretaker of all moral value and philosophy. According to Aristotle, poetry is directly related to the heart and soul."[12]

Plato and Aristotle both cite mimesis in comparison to exegesis, a concept used to tell a story and give a representative description of artistic, literary, or poetic phenomena and events that unveil a plot. Mimesis then evolved into a concept or a process that presents, that shows, and tells. Mimesis directly represents action or a series of actions. Life comprises a multitude of events, phenomena, and plots from situation to situation, experience to experience, one moment in time to another; encountered by individuals throughout their existence.

Socrates was the teacher of Plato, and Plato was the teacher of Aristotle. Plato, as the mentor and teacher to Aristotle, founded and taught at the Academy in Athens, an institution for philosophy, scientific, and mathematical research. Following in the footsteps of Socrates, Plato, and Aristotle, along with Socrates, became known as the big three of society, morality, ethics, virtue, justice, and other ideas relating to human behavior. All three philosophers are important not just because they were the first to think the things they did, but also because their ideas are still influencing us today. The philosophies of Socrates, Plato, and Aristotle are considered to have influence in the construct of Western Civilization. Socrates first introduced a metaphor of Mimesis based on a story of the three beds to give an insight into his concept of mimesis. *Socrates stated that one bed exists as an idea made by God (the Platonic ideal, or form); one bed is made by the carpenter, indicating his perception or imitation of God's idea; and one bed is made by the artist, a drawing or rendition of his perception of the carpenter's perception of God's perception.*[13]

Silent films are another example of the use of Mimesis representation in a way because the viewer has to interpret the plot, without words, based on the silent actor's presentation. The concept of Mimesis as a literary phenomenon became a literary concept that embroiled literary characters in stories and plays. Emplotment is essential to the process of Mimesis. Emplotment is a process or a concept that assembles the entire range of plots and experiences encountered by a literary character and organizes them to depict the interplay of the series of events and how they lead up to the outcome or catharsis. In the context of literature, catharsis is the culmination of an individual's lived experiences that cause an emotional response, revealing the central character's tragic awakening/awareness. Catharsis begins when the individual (the tragic hero) realizes the sequential impact of their actions, then realizes, within their psychology, how their life has turned out with tragic consequences. Catharsis can also occur in revelation as the individual becomes aware of the direction their life is taking, causing the individual to change their life direction or maintain their life course. Catharsis occurs when an individual reflects on the emplotments in their life. Catharsis is the result of an individual reflecting on the entirety of their life experiences and bringing the results of that reflection into their consciousness. The finality of catharsis is the reaction individuals have of themselves at points of reflection. A significant part of catharsis is the response/reaction others have to the individual. In addition to what one thinks of themselves, what do others think about them? Is there alignment between one's personal perspective about themselves and the perspective of others toward the same individual? While most often, the ultimate completion of catharsis occurs in the final stages of life when the individual reflects upon the past life experiences and phenomena they have encountered, and how they have responded. However, catharsis can also occur intermittently throughout life as individuals reflect upon specific incidents or a series of incidents that occur before they enter the twilight of their life. Catharsis can result in a range of emotional reactions: happiness, sadness, depression, fear, surprise, satisfaction, regret, or anger. Catharsis can develop when an individual encounters a life experience that is catastrophic and realizes their life needs to change. Catharsis can be transformational. The key aspect of catharsis is that "it is emotional." The process of catharsis ends when the human earthly existence ends, when death occurs. In the context of this book, emplotments develop during Stage 2 Mimesis. Commonly, reflection and Catharsis are a focus in stage 3 Mimesis. Shakespearean literature is an example of the concepts of emplotment, catharsis, and Mimesis based on the literary narrative of the tragic hero.

Life is a series of encounters with phenomena, a sequence of plots in the lived experience of individuals. Emplotment is how the series of plots in life is woven together to make a narrative of the individual's life. Emplotment does not isolate plots but synergizes them to reveal outcomes that develop, not from one event, but from a series of events. Mimesis represents what the individual is thinking, feeling, and doing at various points in time. Mimesis directly reveals to the audience or the onlooker the nature of the character in question, at particular stages in their life. Mimesis is a representation of the individual's reality at various stages of their life. An objective of Mimesis is to invoke audience or public reaction to the character, situation, or phenomena, to gain audience or public participation and involvement in the development of the entire emplotment of events leading up to the catharsis. Catharsis reveals how the character is affected by the entire series of prior life events.[14]  In life, when others give you advice or feedback on your behavior or actions, that is considered a form of involvement that can reinforce, influence, change, shape, or mold an individual's Mimesis.

Twentieth-century authors used mimesis in relationship to social practice and interpersonal relationships, moving beyond mimesis as a concept of models that imitate inanimate objects, the body, emotions, senses, and the temporal aspects of literary characters and phenomena. The concept of Mimesis began to evolve into a basic concept of the human entity.

Mimesis became a fundamental representation of how humans relate to their world, how humans relate to others, and how others view and respond to humans in relation to their world.[15]

It is interesting to realize how the concept of mimesis has evolved. First, as a reference to mimicry and imitation. Mimesis developed as a means to express beauty in art and poetry as a reference to the beauty in natural endeavors and artistic creativity.  Then, as a concept referring to the narrative of literature that reveals the way humans relate to and are impacted by the experiences and phenomena literary characters encounter in narrative.  Mimesis, then, developed as a representation of the reality of the human being. Mimesis addresses the question of: who am I? Who do others think I am? How does my self-concept align with how others perceive me? Mimesis became a lens that views issues about others through another individual. Who are you? It is a question posed by others in evaluating the reality of another individual. From the perspective of this book, Mimesis became the represented reality in an individual's fundamental process of living life and the perception of how a specific individual and other individuals evaluate and analyze the life being lived. Mimesis is constructed from birth through adulthood. Mimesis construction is an ongoing process from birth throughout life. In the Volumes I – IV of the Three-Fold Mimesis of Life, the term Mimesis is used to identify the integral aspect of understanding the human evolution from birth throughout the human life cycle. It unveils the journey in constructing the human reality.

## The Evolution of Mimesis

Paul Ricoeur (1913-2005) first introduced the formal concept of the Three-Fold Mimesis. Ricoeur was a French philosopher. He served as the John Nuveen Professor Emeritus in the Divinity School at Chicago's Divinity School from 1971 until his retirement in 1991.

Ricoeur's combined phenomenological description with hermeneutics (Hermeneutical Phenomenology). This concept reveals Ricoeur's vision of how the description and interpretation of events, actions, and behaviors are important to give an accurate presentation of their meaning, intent, and to construct accuracy for feedback. Ricoeur wrote the book *"Time and Narrative."* He presents the alignment between time and narrative. The two concepts combine to recount the life of an individual. An individual's life is described in a narrative over time. Ricoeur envisioned a narrative as a means to tell a story about an individual's life. A narrative can also describe how others perceive the life of an individual. Essentially, Ricoeur advanced the effect of narrative to answer the questions "who? Who is this? Who said that? Who did that? Who is that? Who are we?" Who am I?"[16] and what does it all mean? In his discussion of a Three-Fold hermeneutic process of Mimesis, Ricoeur generalized the process in terms of pre-configuration, configuration, and reconfiguration.[17]

Ricoeur's argument is that narrative can describe an individual's life. The catalyst to Ricoeur's creative thinking regarding the relationship of narrative to life combines with the concept of time. Narration can express Human behavior, but human behavior is an ongoing sequence of events that occurs over time into the future of the individuals' lifespan. To capture the reality of an individual, one has to consider the series of events an individual encounters. Understanding how an individual responds to those series of events and evaluating the human response hermeneutically is critical to understanding the reality of that individual. Ricoeur further advanced that "The narrative representing an individual's actions and experiences is revealed in the three stages of interpretation: prefiguration (Mimesis 1), configuration (Mimesis 2), and re-figuration[2] (Mimesis3).[18] The narrative of an individual takes place within a finite scope of time. The narrative and the time individuals construct their Mimesis vary.

Time as a concept is only relevant in the consciousness of an individual. The concept of time does not exist for an individual before that individual is born, nor does it exist after the individual ceases to live. Time as a concept only exists within the timeframe (lifecycle) of an individual, as long as the individual exists. The Mimesis construction of an individual's life is finite. Consequently, narrative describes the life of an individual, their Mimesis, their reality, within the context of the time they exist. The *Three-Fold Mimesis of Life* is an accounting of the stages and evolution in an individual's life experiences within the time frame of their conscious existence. An individual, in their lived experiences, the decisions and choices they make, and the associations they

[2] A new or different relative arrangement of parts or elements: the rearrangement of a previous configuration. Also see Endnote for the meaning of re-figuration.

choose, essentially feed the narrative of their life. The way an individual lives can be considered a narrative of their life. They, themselves, will reflect on their life narrative, as well as others, intermittently throughout their life and in the twilight years of their life. This book considers Mimesis the creation of an individual's life narrative.

*The unique aspect of this concept is that individuals have the opportunity to create their own story, to write their own narrative. Understanding this concept at an early age can mitigate much of the ambiguity and uncertainty in life and give individuals direction and purpose as they live their lives.*

Ricoeur's concept of the dynamics of Mimesis theory made it relevant as a tool applicable to give narrative to real life and real-life experiences, though Ricoeur's use of Mimesis was used to conceptualize the narrative of literary characters, primarily in the religious and theological realm.

*Application of Mimesis to real-life experiences is what this book and volumes of the Three-Fold Mimesis of Life are intended to motivate individuals to do with their lives. An individual's Mimesis, constructed with positive aforethought, can lead to productive and satisfying lived experiences and a productive and satisfying life.*

Ricoeur placed a high value on time and an accurate narrative description. Many young people take the value of time for granted. Time becomes more valuable as we age and have less of it, analogous to the supply and demand theory. For products and services in demand, the more supply, the less valuable. The less supply, the more valuable. The supply and demand theory is not only relevant to economics. It is relevant to life. Ricoeur's concept of time and narrative aligns as a Segway into *"the Three-Fold Mimesis of Life"*:

> *"History has meaning because human actions produce meanings. When these meanings are continuous over the generations of human time. This continuity, in turn, is felt in the human experience of time organized as future, past, and present rather than as mere serial consecution."* [19]

Time is also a fleeting concept. The best way an individual can predict the future is to understand the past. Time has an ambiguous quality according to Ricoeur. The past is gone. The future has yet to come. The present is questionable in its existence because it is in constant motion into the future. The past and future have a tangible quality. The present does not, according to Ricoeur. The reader does not need to get hung up on this ambiguity, but the reader does need to understand the relationship between Mimesis construction and Time. The past has a reality because it is reflective. The future has a reality because it is perceptive and based on past experiences. The future has ambiguity, according to Riceour, because it is in constant motion into the future. *"This moment"* is gone and no longer exists, according to Ricoeurian logic.

The lived experiences of individuals are grounded in the individual's experience with time. Time facilitates the construction of Mimesis. The emplotment of an individual's lived experiences and how they utilize time engaging lived experiences they encounter, constructs their Mimesis, Stage 1, Stage 2, and Stage 3.

Complementary to the concepts of Mimesis, narrative, and emplotment is Hermeneutical Phenomenology. Ricoeur, along with Martin Heidegger, expanded on the concept of Phenomenology. Phenomenology is a concept developed by Edmund Husserl. It refers to the study of experiences (incidents, situations/phenomena), an individual encounters in their life, their behavior, their actions, and their responses to life experiences they encounter, which represent phenomena. Phenomenology studies conscious acts of observation that an individual encounters, as well as the behavior they consciously demonstrate. The goal of phenomenology is to understand the integral motives of the acts of an individual(s), to interpret the acts in conjunction with behavior and behavior patterns, "and to understand and interpret the objective entities that correspond to them."[20] A Phenomenon or phenomena are an act or acts (encounters) in an individual's lived experience (synergized together they are also known as emplotments). Hermeneutics refers to the manner in which the narrative presents phenomena, the accuracy of the narrative representation, and the accuracy of how the narrative is interpreted, described. The recounting of the words, expressions, metaphors, and analogies involved in describing phenomena is important to accurate understanding. The point is that how narrative describes phenomena gives the receiver of the description an impression/perception of the object, person, or situation. Therefore, it is important to describe phenomena or interpret the behavior or actions accurately. Presenting narrative accurately in descriptive terms (hermeneutically) is important to the process of Mimesis. The concept of Hermeneutical Phenomenology focuses on the accurate representation of events, phenomena, human behaviors, and lived experiences. It is critical to the concept of Mimesis, as a representation of the human reality, to present the emplotments in an individual's lived experiences accurately. Hermeneutics involves the interpretation of language, body language, facial expression, voice tone, moral intent, allegorical interpretation, and anagogical interpretation. Hermeneutical interpretation of human phenomenology encompasses a range of factors to enable the observer to be able to, accurately, give meaning to an individual's actions and intent. Mimesis is a concept resulting from the thoughts, behavior, identities, and realities of human beings. For example, when a civil rights demonstrator was killed by a White racist in Charlottesville, Virginia, and Donald Trump stated, "There are very fine people on both sides."[21] Some people will consider this statement hermeneutically accurate. Some will consider it hermeneutically not true because they believe all racists are considered deplorable people. Some people will appreciate Trump for not maligning racists. Some people will abhor Trump for not maligning racists. Some people will say Trump was being objective. Some will say that Donald Trump has racist tendencies and is a racist sympathizer. The hermeneutics describing phenomena makes a difference in how the narrative is received. Additionally, individuals interpret narratives based on their social location, background, and lived experiences. In Donald Trump's case, stating, "There are very fine people on both sides", is probably accurate. Only one individual committed the racist crime. We do not know the intentions of the hundreds of people present at the demonstration on both sides. We can only deduce the negative intentions based on the negative behavior of one individual who killed a demonstrator. Therefore, objectively, there very well could have been good people on both sides. However, realistically, if people support racism and racists, they are generally perceived as racists themselves. Then the question then becomes, is being racist a good or bad thing? Among other racists, they are considered good people among the general population, and anti-hate individuals; they are considered deplorable.

# Three-Fold Mimesis (Paul Riceour's Version)

This author was introduced to the Three-Fold Mimesis while in graduate school studying for a Master's degree in Religious Studies at the University of Chicago Divinity School. Academically, Mimesis evolved and is presented as a terminology to give expression, understanding, and insight into the characters portrayed in text and literature. While studying the works of Paul Ricoeur, this author realized that the concept of Mimesis is relevant not only to religious and theological literature, imitative art and literature, or mimicry as used by Plato and Aristotle, but Mimesis as a concept is relevant to real life. Riceour's advanced and contributed to the concept of Mimesis in terms of *"The Three-Fold Mimesis"*, Hermeneutics, Phenomenology, Hermeneutical Phenomenology, Time and Narrative; all in the context of how they contribute to framing the life and lived experiences of individuals from a literary perspective.

*"The Three-Fold Mimesis of Life"* is the process that brings together, conceptualizes, and understands the meaning, relationship, and relevance of each aspect of the plots in life (lived experiences). A good example of the literary application of the Three-Fold Mimesis is William Shakespeare's Tragedies. The tragic hero is the center of emplotment. Emplotment and narratives describe the experiences of the tragic hero. Finally, there is the revelation of the tragedy. A tragic ending involves a catharsis of emotion when the plot reveals to the audience the fate of the tragic hero. The tragic hero has a cathartic response. The audience completes the Mimesis with their response or reaction to the tragic hero. When the audience responds to the fate of the tragic hero, the Mimesis of the Shakespearean tragedy is completed. In the Shakespearean and Ricoeurian concept of Mimesis, a key factor is audience involvement, for the audience or reader to respond to the circumstance

of the tragic hero. While academically, Mimesis is presented as a theory, a process that is experienced without aforethought. In the concept of Mimesis presented in this book, *"The Three-Fold Mimesis of Life"*, aforethought is an important factor for an individual in creating their Mimesis.

The author of this book presents Mimesis as a practical concept that an individual can apply to their own life. An individual can be an agent or a catalyst to the construction of their own reality. An individual's Mimesis can be constructed with themselves as agents and with aforethought. An individual's Mimesis can be constructed with aforethought instead of being an ongoing random series of actions and reactions to lived experiences they encounter (Ricoeurian Mimesis). An individual can construct their reality by selecting the lived experiences that engage them, instead of allowing their lived experiences to occur with haphazard participation by the individual. With aforethought, the individual can respond to the lived experiences they encounter based on their goals in life. This author presents a proactive conceptualization to Mimesis construction as opposed to viewing Mimesis as an analytical concept in literature or for analyzing the life of a character or individual(s) posthumously or hypothetically in a literary context (Ricoeurian).

Ricoeur saw Mimesis as a reactionary literary concept to give conceptualization to characters in literature (primarily from a religious theological viewpoint) and beyond mimicry of an inanimate entity and beyond the masterful poetic revelation of reality void of practical association (Socrates, Plato, Aristotle). The author of this book is advancing the concept that the individual themselves can be catalysts and agents to their Mimesis construction by exercising aforethought. Conceptualizing Mimesis in real time instead of in past time (reflectively or reactively) or as a mimic representing a thing in nature or a poetic expression allows the individual to determine how their life will develop. This allows individuals to become catalysts and agents to determine their own Mimesis construction, to determine their own reality. Plato and Aristotle viewed Mimesis as a component of nature, art, and poetry. Mimesis to them Mimesis encapsulated artistic beauty.

Paul Ricoeur's concept of Mimesis is literarily focused on the reactionary concepts of the human response to their lived experiences and phenomena they encountered in hindsight. Ricoeur also experienced the concept of Mimesis in a religious context, in alignment with the concept of exegesis. Ricoeur saw Mimesis as a product of an unfolding set of factors in literature. Mimesis to Ricoeur was a result of the phenomena encountered by the literary character; how the character responded to the phenomena they encountered, and the occurring and recurring phenomena to which the characters responded, is interpreted. The individual's Mimesis is revealed by the accumulation of emplotments that construct the narrative of their life and lived experiences. Emplotments are a narrative strategy that organizes events into a meaningful whole by giving them structure, coherence, and causality. Ricoeur viewed Mimesis to evaluate and analyze past lived experiences of literary characters as a narrative of their life.

Dr. Barnes presents Mimesis as applicable to the present and future real-life lived experiences, with the past either reinforcing present and future experiences or being a catalyst that affects and changes present and future behaviors. This presentation of Mimesis is different from the concept of Mimesis as imagery, a representation of inanimate objects, or a component of nature, art, or poetry. It is different from evaluating the human condition in hindsight. Dr. Barnes suggests that individuals can construct their Mimesis, present and future lived experiences, instead of reacting to lived experiences and phenomena they encounter. In other words, applying the aforethought concept of Mimesis construction, humans have the ability to be agents and catalysts in how their life turns out.

## Stages of the Three-Fold Mimesis [22]

### From the Literature Perspective and In terms of the Human Lived Experiences

**Mimesis Stage 1 (Literary)** involves the understanding of structures, symbols, temporality, the environment and setting. Focus is on the actions not the characters. Mimesis Stage 1, in reference to literature, sets the stage for the development and unfolding of the plot (Mimesis 2 and 3).

**Mimesis Stage 1 (In the lived experiences of human beings)** is the infant stage, birth, and the early developmental stages of life. In Mimesis Stage 1, the child is dependent on parental or caregiver influence. Mimesis 1 lays the foundation for subsequent developments in Stage 2.

**Mimesis Stage 2 (Literary)** gives further extension of mimesis 1. The plot is developed. It pulls together and gives understanding of how the successive actions relate to each other and fit together. It gives meaning to the symbols, structures, and temporality of the environment and situational context unveiled in mimesis 1. In addition, mimesis 2 acts as a connection, a bridge between mimesis 1 and mimesis 3 that allows the audience to understand and conceptualize the meaning of the narrative. Mimesis 2 sets the stage for what occurs in mimesis 3. Mimesis 2 displays the emplotments of phenomena experienced.

**Mimesis Stage 2 (In the lived experiences of human beings)** is the accumulation of lived experiences and an ongoing reaction and response to the lived experiences and phenomena individuals encounter. The longest stage of Mimesis is from early childhood (5-7 years old), when the child has contact outside of caregiver influence, until stage 3 Mimesis (senior). The accumulation of lived experiences and human responses to lived experiences is what constructs the Mimesis of the individual. The lived experiences and reactions to lived experiences determine the reality of the individual, how the individual perceives themselves, and how others perceive the individual.

**Mimesis Stage 3 (Literary)** gives full meaning to the narrative. It is where suffering occurs, the plot unfolds, and a catharsis of emotion occurs. However, the unique aspect of mimesis 3 is audience participation (other people's response to who and what they perceive the tragic hero to have become or experienced). Audience reaction is necessary to give meaning to the entire narrative. The reaction of the audience is critical for the Mimesis to have meaning. Stage 3 Mimesis represents the point in the cycle of emplotments when one is completely vested in their lived experiences. They experience the resultant outcome of the emplotments in their life.

The combination of all three Mimesis represents the Three-Fold Mimesis. When whom we think we are, whom others see us as being, align, then our reality emerges. There is stability in our Mimesis. We realized our true selves. An individual's introspection, retrospection, and reflection on his or her own life is part of Stage 3 Mimesis. Mimesis 3 reveals the logical culmination/result of the emplotments in Mimesis 1 and 2.

**Mimesis Stage 3 (In the lived experience of human beings)** is the reflection stage. It is the stage when individuals reflect back on their life and evaluate their lived experiences and how they responded. It is also the stage where other people have a perception of the lived experiences of the individual. Other people are also in position to evaluate their perception of the individual. They are near the end of life's path that will define their existence. Their life takes form. They have chosen a way of life, a profession, a job, a mindset, a behavior pattern, and have consistency in their daily life. Other perceptions have a fermented regarding the individual. In order to give full meaning to the choices one has made, the responses, feedback, and opinions of others are necessary to complete the definition of who one has become. Often, the notion of who we think we are, who others see us as being, do not align. Alignment occurs when our self-concept agrees with the opinions of others about who we are. If those perceptions are not aligned or different, there is confusion in one's life.

## The Relationship between the Three-Fold Mimesis of Life and Lived Experiences

**Mimesis** is the representation of an individual's reality in the Stage 1, Stage 2 and Stage 3, stages of Mimesis construction. Mimesis is a dynamic phenomenon. The human Mimesis evolves as the individual evolves. This author also considers Mimesis to represent the human applications to the process of an individual configuring the progress, process and evolution through their stages in life. *"The Three-Fold Mimesis of Life"* is about the progress of life from the beginning to the end. The Theories of psychology give parents and caregivers insight into the foundational developmental process important for a child to have the tools that allow them to construct a functional and positive Mimesis. If Stage 1 Mimesis is properly constructed, when the child enters Stage 2 Mimesis, the child will have an advantage as an agent and catalyst in constructing their Mimesis throughout Stage 2.

This author is applying the concept of Mimesis to an individual's practical lived experiences. Investigating the lives of real people (Volume III) in the framework and concept of Mimesis will give the reader understanding of how Mimesis is applicable to their lived experiences and the lived experiences to be encountered of those yet to be born. The concept of Mimesis began with regard to art forms. In plays presented in the time of Plato and Aristotle, Aristotle as a student of Plato, continued to present Mimesis in the concept of an art form. Where human's represented inanimate objects to give scenery and background to plays, to give a reality to the meaning of the play. Humans mimicked and represented inanimate objects. As stated earlier, Aristotle and Plato presented the concept of Mimesis as an "imitation" of inanimate objects, as a mimicry of things.

Then during the era of academia, Paul Riceour conveyed Mimesis as a concept in literature. To give meaning to the message presented in literature. The stages of the human experience in literature. Ricouer explained, through Mimesis, the plight and significance of humans in literature presentation. Riceour's intent was to allow readers of literature (often religious literature) to understand the meaning of what they read. The Shakespearian tragic heroes, even analyzing the life of Jesus Christ can be conceptualized through Mimesis.  Riceour presented The Three-Fold Mimesis as the process that brings together, conceptualizes, and gives meaning and understanding to the relationship and relevance of each aspect of the plots in lived experiences of individuals represented in literature. Riceour presented Mimesis as an analysis of the lived experiences of literary characters.

This author is conceptualizing Mimesis as being applicable to real life, to convey the Stages an individual experiences from the time they are born through the time they die. Riceour presented Mimesis as a literary concept to understand the emplotments in the past lived experiences of an individual's life as presented in literature. This author presents and conceptualizes Mimesis as Stages that represent the reality in the lived experiences of individuals. In books, Volumes 1-IV, *"The Three-Fold Mimesis of Life"*, Mimesis is presented as a concept that explains how the lived experiences and phenomena an individual encounters in their lifetime represents their human reality. Lived experiences that individuals encounter are emplotments. The narrative of an individual's life is conceptualized in the series of their lived experiences (emplotments) the individual encounters and responds. Understanding Mimesis in real time instead of past-time allows the individual to determine how their life will develop. The individual can determine who they will become. Perceiving the concept of Mimesis in this way, advances the notion that an individual has the ability to construct their Mimesis and therefore determine their reality. Riceour's concept of Mimesis is focused on the reactionary concepts of the human response to their lived experiences and phenomena they encountered. The difference between the use of Mimesis by Plato / Aristotle, Riceour and Dr. Ronald Barnes is that Dr. Barnes presents Mimesis as applicable to present and future lived experiences, different from the concept of Aristotle's and Plato's Mimesis, as representation of inanimate objects or as poetic imagery. Dr. Barnes suggest that individuals can construct their Mimesis and future lived experiences, with aforethought, instead of reacting to lived experiences and phenomena they encounter or viewing Mimesis to evaluate and analyze past lived experiences of literary characters, as Riceour presented in his application of Mimesis. In other words, humans have the ability to be agents and catalyst in how their life turns out. This is not anything new. "I am the master of my fate", is a common expression. The point is that some people are the masters of their fate, most people are not.

## The Three-Fold Mimesis of an individual's Life is the Representation of that Individual's evolution, development and reality

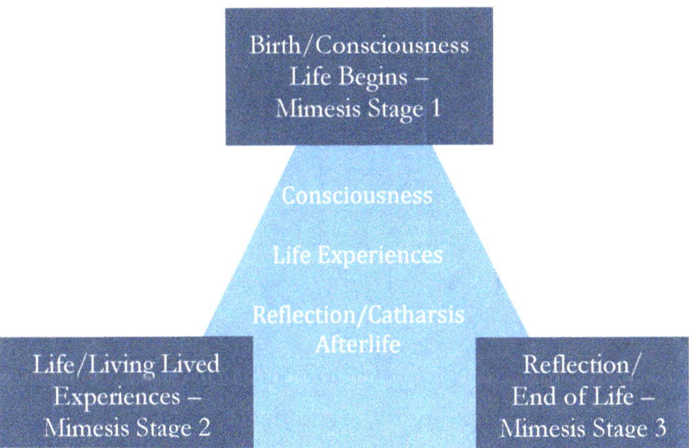


An individual's reality has been represented in a number of ways. For Aristotle and Plato, representation becomes man's way of being in the world and his method of learning. Plato, on the other hand, viewed representation as a medium or channel through which man gets to 'the real', about the world, others and especially himself.[23] The concept of "representation" in psychology refers to the truth to express the assumption that individuals do not act on the basis of "objective" or generalized patterns of the world, but on the basis of their specific "internal representations". In psychology the hermeneutical presentation is the representation of an individual is their reality.[24] Keep in mind that different people may interpret phenomena differently.

**Stage 1 Mimesis** begins at birth, the beginning of consciousness. It is the shortest Mimesis stage but a significantly critical stage because it lays the foundation for an individual's life. The child's only reality is based in their existence and need for care, their entire openness to learn. The child becomes a result of their parents / caregivers influence in Stage 1 Mimesis. The individual's reality is being created in Stage 1 Mimesis. In Stage 1 Mimesis, the "baby" experiences the shaping and molding of their personality development. The baby is a blank canvass, to mold into an individual by teaching behavior, implanting ideas, thoughts, instincts, values, norms, ethics, morals and a cognitive foundation based on the nature of the parent or caregiver. Stage one Mimesis last as long as the child is under the exclusive care of the parent or caregiver. An individual has no control over the social location in which they come into consciousness. They can be born into poverty. They can be born into privilege. They can be born into a single parent home. They can be born and placed into adoption. They can be born with deformity. They can be a result of an unwanted pregnancy. The situation in which an individual comes into consciousness is outside or their influence or control.

Genetics can influence how a child develops. However, genetics is just one piece of the development puzzle that shapes and molds a child's Mimesis and personality. Environmental variables including parenting, culture, education, and social relationships play a vitally significant role.[25]

Exposures of an individual to outside influences, begins Stage 2 Mimesis. Stage 2 Mimesis is the beginning of an individual's exercising control over their life. The period in which they begin to make decisions for themselves is the longest lasting period of Mimesis.

**Stage 2 Mimesis** involves the accumulation of Life experiences that develop the person you are into the person you will become. It is the Stage full of phenomena, involving the accumulation of life experiences and the way individuals respond to the phenomena they encounter. Stage 2 Mimesis starts when the individual begins to create their own life experiences, when they encounter phenomena outside of the home and oversight of their parents and caregivers. Stage 2 Mimesis is encompassing, challenging and substantial. It last for the majority of an individual's lifetime, until the individual becomes a senior citizens and enters Stage 3 Mimesis. In Stage 2, individuals experience their "Becoming" (who they will be), Individual's experience who they are and whom they will further become, depending on the phenomena encountered and how they respond to the phenomena, they encounter. Stage 2 Stage 2 Mimesis is a continuation of the human development process. Stage 2 is dynamic. One difference between Stage 1 and Stage 2 development is that in Stage 2 development, the individual becomes an agent and catalyst to their development process. The individual has determination over their Mimesis construction. Mimesis 2 begins when the child is exposed to influence outside of parental or guardian oversight. When they attend nursery school or kindergarten. The individual evolves in Stage 2. The stage 2 evolution of the individual should result in the stabilization of their reality.

**Stage 3** Mimesis is the period of Mimesis that last as long as the memory of the individual, from senior citizen, reflecting on their own life, until death (the Final Mimesis), and on into the afterlife, as long as others keep their memory alive. How many of you in Stage 3 Mimesis, look back on your life and realize how fleeting life is? When your memory is no longer alive then, for you, Stage 3 Mimesis ends. The combination of all three stages comprise the ***The Three-Fold Mimesis of Life Individually Profiled:***

Volume III gives practical insights into the Mimesis of noteworthy individuals so the reader can better understand the concept of Mimesis and the Mimesis constructions that engaged their lived experiences, as well as the Mimesis constructs that resulted in the outcomes of their lived experiences and phenomena they encounters. The response of lived experiences and phenomena they have encountered is also described in the profiles of these noteworthy individuals. Their profile descriptions reveal their socialization process and environment (both their immediate environment and the society environment) that influenced their Mimesis of life.

A review and analysis of the profiles of the following individuals will give the reader and insight into their own Mimesis.

***Dr. Martin Luther King, Jr., Muhammed Ali, Oprah Winfrey, Barak Hussein Obama, Billy Graham, Queen Elizabeth II, Richard Nixon, Malcolm X, Stanley "Tookie" Williams, Donald Trump, Jay-Z, Tupac Shakur, Elvis Presley, Beyonce, Marilyn Monroe.***

The reader will gain insight into how these individuals constructed their Mimesis within the environment they existed, based on their lived experiences and the phenomena they encountered. The lived experiences these individuals engaged and how response to their lived experiences constructed and affected their Mimesis. Hopefully the reader will understand the benefits of constructing their own Mimesis in relationship to their environment, resulting in a positive, satisfying and productive life.

## The Time Factor of Mimesis

The concept of Mimesis is integrated into the time cycle of life. Human beings are "cursed" with a conscious awareness of their mortality. People know they will die within a generally defined period of time. The time period for Mimesis construction is finite. Robert W. Firestone, Ph.D. advances the following argument on the effect of mortality awareness.[26]

> "I believe that the tragedy of the human condition is that people's awareness and true self-consciousness concerning this existential issue contributes to an ultimate irony: Human beings are both brilliant and aberrant, sensitive and savage, exquisitely caring and painfully indifferent, remarkably creative and incredibly destructive to self and others. The capacity to imagine and conceptualize has negative as well as positive consequences because they predispose anxiety states that culminate in a defensive form of denial."

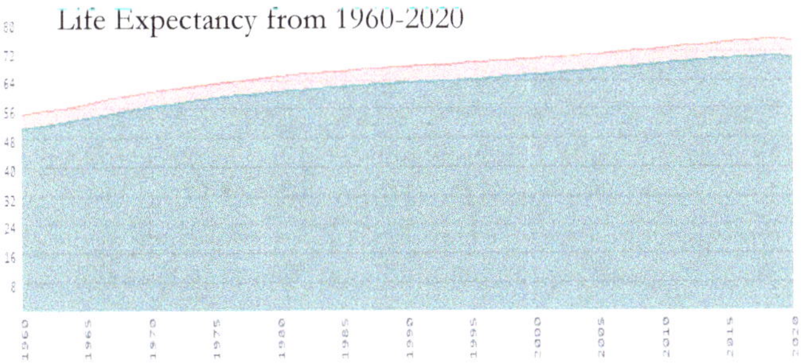

Life Expectancy from 1960-2020

The point that Dr. Firestone makes is that because humans have awareness of their limited life span and that their lifetime is finite, this awareness causes a human dilemma, a duality that impacts Mimesis construction. Humans construct a number of psychological defenses. Often the defenses humans create are contrary to a balanced Mimesis construction. Dr. Firestone advances that human awareness of their mortality causes them to behave in paradoxical patterns. The irony of the human condition is that human awareness and self-consciousness concerning this existential issue contributes to an ultimate irony: "Human beings are both brilliant and aberrant, sensitive and savage, exquisitely caring and painfully indifferent, remarkably creative and incredibly destructive to self and others." The capacity to imagine and conceptualize has negative as well as positive consequences because they predispose states of anxiety that culminate in a defensive form of denial. Observation of the phenomena in the world that occurs on a daily basis reinforces duality in human behavior. One would think that because life is limited and people are aware of the finite time frame of their existence, they would behave and interact in the most productive and positive ways. Reality confirms humans often think and behave contrary to what is harmonious interaction.[27] Why do humans rob banks instead of work to get money? Then again, MOST people do work, instead of rob banks to get money.

Because an individual's lifetime is limited. Awareness of an individual's mortality creates limitations. In stage 1 Mimesis the child is dependent on the parent or caregiver. The **Zone of Proximal Development (ZPD)** is "the space between what a learner can do without assistance and what a learner can do with adult guidance or in collaboration with more capable peers"[28] A child's development and learning of skills are significantly dependent on their parent or caregiver. While the scaffolding (the process that helps people learn, achieve goals, solve problems, or complete tasks that they might not be able to do on their own) support given to the child by the caregiver or parent is temporary, it will influence their developmental process throughout their life. As individuals evolve from Mimesis Stage 1 and throughout Mimesis Stage 2, they will experience new learning. New learning takes place from engaging new lived experiences, new phenomena and from interacting with new and different people who have different ideals and skills. The interaction with new experience by an individual and the new learning they receive as a result of that experience in the zone of proximal development. The space and time in which individuals experiences new learning facilitated by their encounter with other people or a new experience in their lived experience is their **ZPD**. Because individual's have a limited amount of time to learn, accomplish, succeed and live, there are limitations to their learning and applications of what they learn. The temporal characteristic of life causes individual's to become more conscious and place more value on their life as they age. Individuals who realize their time on this earth is temporal and who stay conscious about the limit to their lifetime experiences and contact with individuals they engage are more focused to optimize their **ZPD.** They give more focus and aforethought to constructing their Mimesis. They have an advantage over those who live life haphazard and merely react to phenomena they encounter. During Stage 2 Mimesis, individuals construct the majority of their Life Mimesis. Both an individual's Stage 2 Mimesis and ZPD are temporal states of being embedded in the individual's life**time**. **Time** being the key factor.[29] The effective value of **ZPD** is based on and controlled by how an individual uses their lifetime.

The **Zone of Mimesis Development (ZMD)** is different from ZPD. ZMD takes place over an individual's lifetime from birth during the process of Social Referencing and throughout their lifetime into their Stage 3 Mimesis. ZMD postulates that new learning is a lifelong process. An individual never gets too old to learn nor does an individual possess complete knowledge. Understanding this concept is foundation for keeping an open mind. An open mind allows new learning to enter. A closed mind keeps individuals in a static state of being.

"Society manifest a multitude of psychological defenses, and it is these defenses and their subsequent damage to other people that is perpetuated in the world at large. Often human behavior manifest incidents of failures to achieve empathy and compassion for others. Greed, dishonesty, outright prejudice, ethnic cleansing" behaviors, and religious warfare, racism, actions that promote inequality and violence are destructive to formulating positive human traits. The appropriate education about our psychological defenses, how they are formed, and how they function is essential to achieving insight into the subject of ethics, morality and positive Mimesis construction. People with a positive orientation can shape a peaceful world that illustrates concern and equality for all.[30]

The time when one is born can be considered a dependent factor in the Mimesis of Life because the Mimesis of Life begins at birth. When a human comes into consciousness is Mimesis Stage 1. When an individual enters consciousness depends on when the man and woman copulate and that process creates a successful birth. The child is also dependent on their parents or caregivers for laying the foundation of their Mimesis. The social location at which an individual is born is dependent on their birth parents.

Mimesis stage 2 can be considered a dependent variable factor in the Mimesis of Life because the lived experiences an individual encounters will vary, according to environment, phenomena encountered, associations, education, culture, and decisions made by parents or caregivers, and the developmental process the child experiences. The Human response to the lived experiences and phenomena they encounter is also variable. Stage 2 Mimesis is the longest period of Mimesis. It last from the time an individual experiences phenomena outside of the supervision of their parents or caregivers until the individual enters senior citizen status, the reflective state, Stage 3 Mimesis. During the time Stage 2 Mimesis last, the individual is confronted with multiple situations and phenomena that require them to respond and make life impacting decisions. Because Stage 2 Mimesis is the longest in terms of time, it is stage 2 Mimesis that is the critical determinate period in which the individual is defined. The *Zone of Mimesis Development is most active during Stage 2 Mimesis.* ZPD and ZMD can occur simultaneously. Normally, ZPD occurs with another person being a catalyst to another individual's new learning. ZMD can occur when an individual simple has a new experience or encounters phenomena that impacts their thinking, perspective and behavior. An individual's Mimesis can experience changes during the stage 2 period. Stage 2 last long enough for an individual to change life directions. They can reconstruct their perception of themselves and the perception others have of them.   Based on the average life cycle of an individual, Stage 2 Mimesis last from age 5 to approximately senior citizen age (60, 65, 70 and older). The world average age of death is a few years lower at 69.8 years for men and 74.9 years for women. Within the European Union, the average life span is 77.8 and 83.3 years respectively. In the United States the average lifespan is 72 years and 78 years respectively for men and women. Birth rate and death rate are given in births/deaths per 1,000 inhabitants within one year. The table below shows the official data from the year 2020.[31] An individual's Mimesis of Life is based on how they respond to lived experiences encountered during their life**time.**

While the Stages of Mimesis are determined by time, they are not defined by time. The Mimesis of Life is defined by an individual's developmental process, how an individual constructs their reality, their life, the decisions they make in life based on the phenomena they are confronted with, how they respond to the phenomena and how individuals perceive themselves and how others perceive them.  How the individual utilizes the time in their life is determines the choices they make and it is the choices they make that gives definition to their Mimesis.  Time is a limitation to Mimesis construction.  The Mimesis of an individual's Life is influenced by their schema, the psychology, cognitive and behavioral, patterns of thought and patterns of behavior that organizes categories of information about individuals and the relationships they develop during their life.

Stage 3 Mimesis is a dependent factor in the time process of life, dependent on prior lived experiences and the human response to those experiences.  Normally, Stage 3 Mimesis begins at the senior citizen time of life (retirement age 65 or 70 until death and, technically, last until the individual is no longer a memory). If an individual is born, it is inevitable they will die. The Final Mimesis of Stage 3 (death) is an independent variable and can occur prematurely, at any time during the life cycle, even when the individual's life ends prematurely; such as automobile accidental death, death due to sickness, murders, suicides are examples of Final Mimesis occurring prematurely.

Chapter 2

# The Foundation of the Mimesis of Life

## The Psychological Foundation of Mimesis Construction

*"The Three-Fold Mimesis of Life"* refers to the life cycle of an individual. Mimesis is a representation of an individual's reality, as perceived by the individual and as perceived by others. When the perception the individual has of themselves aligns with the perception others have of them, then that is their reality. The three stages of Mimesis are:

**Stage 1)** Coming into consciousness, the inherited social location the individual was born into. Mimesis begins with consciousness. Stage 1 Mimesis is influenced by the child's interactions with the parents or guardians.

**Stage 2)** The longest period of Mimesis. Stage 2 is influenced by what the individual learns and internalizes in Stage 1. The majority of lived experiences, phenomena occur during Stage 2. How the individual responds to the lived experiences and phenomena they encounter is what determines how their Mimesis is constructed. The individual has agency over many of the Life experiences they encounter. Stage 2 can include events of catharsis. Stage 2 catharsis often results in new thinking and behavior change.

**Stage 3)** Stage 3 Mimesis involves the individual reflecting back on their life. Stage 3 also involves how the individual is perceived and evaluated by others who look back on their life. Stage 3 primarily occurs in the latter stage of the life cycle. Stage 3

Mimesis includes the death perceptions of the individual. This stage is also reflective for the individual, looking back on their life, realistically evaluating themselves.

**The Final Mimesis** begins with death and ends when the memory of the individual is dissolved.

Pre-existing cultural conditions are inherited upon coming into this world, from birth. One's parents may be Black, White, Hispanic, or Asian; rich or poor, English, Irish, African, African American, Spanish, Mexican, American, religious, or non-religious. This is a situation that individuals have no control over. The individual comes into an inherited circumstance. As the individual develops and accumulates life experiences, encounters phenomena, they have the right and agency to choose, to change the ways in which they relate to their inherited circumstance. Humans learns concepts and ideologies that determine the way they deal with the life experiences and phenomena they encounter. Individuals have the right of choice, the freedom to decide. The decisions they make throughout life determine their life direction and define them as a person, which creates and forms an image and perception of the individual that is perceived and responded to by others. Consider life as a narrative. Every day of an individual's life adds textual and contextual additions to the narrative of their life. Daily, another chapter is created, and pages are added to an existing chapter. Initially, the individual's story is written for them. Then, as individuals mature, they have the freedom to write their own narrative of life, based on how they respond to their lived experiences, the phenomena they encounter in life, and the decisions they make in responding to their life circumstances.

Volume III explores the life cycle and Mimesis evolution of fifteen high-profile individuals in order to give a practical, rather than theoretical insight into Mimesis.

Dr. Martin Luther King Jr., a minister and civil rights leader

Muhammad Ali, a great boxer and champion of social justice

Oprah Winfrey, television personality, business entrepreneur, and philanthropist,

Barack Obama, 44th President of the United States of America

Rev. Billy Graham, an evangelist, minister, and moral leader

Queen Elizabeth, Queen of England and Queen of the United Kingdom Commonwealth

Malcom X, Minister of the Nation of Islam and civil rights leader

Richard Nixon, 37th President of the United States of America

Stanley "Tookie" Williams, founder and leader of the Crips street gang

Donald Trump, businessman and 45th and 47th President of the United States of America.

Jay-Z, American rapper and businessman

Tupac Shakur, American rapper, actor

Elvis Presley, American singer, actor, entertainer, the king of rock n roll

Beyonce, American singer, performer, entertainer, actor

Marilyn Monroe, American actress

An examination of the life of each of the individuals mentioned above will give insight into the process and concept of "The Three-Fold Mimesis" as applied to the life cycle of these people. Each of these people inherited a station in life. They encountered experiences and phenomena that challenged them as individuals. They made decisions regarding how to deal with their lived experiences. A brief exploration through the mimesis cycle of each of these individuals will illustrate how individuals consciously construct their ontology and the reactions that construction garners from others both in the short term and the long term. The **ontology** of an individual is a component of their Mimesis, a representation of their reality. [32]

> **Ontology**, as a branch of philosophy, is the science of what is, of the kinds and structures of objects. In simple terms, ontology seeks the classification and explanation of entities. Ontology is about the object of inquiry, what you set to examine. Attitude and ideology are synonyms for ontology. In the case of Mimesis, ontology refers to the components of their Mimesis construction (attitude, beliefs, opinions, and mental traits).

## Life Experiences Influence Mimesis

The life experiences (influences) individuals encounter and respond to, determines the construction of their Mimesis. The Three-folds of their Mimesis is strongly influenced by how their developmental process by parents or caregivers and subsequent stage 2 life experiences shape and mold their psychology, how their psychology shapes and molds their response to lived experiences. Integral to these interdependencies is the individual's developmental process in Mimesis. Individuals enter consciousness as babies with a mental blank slate. Psychology and Behavior have a symbiotic relationship. The difference between a good person and a bad person, functional and dysfunctional, can be how the parent or caregiver fills the blank slates. How people think translates into how they behave and how people behave is manifested in how they think.

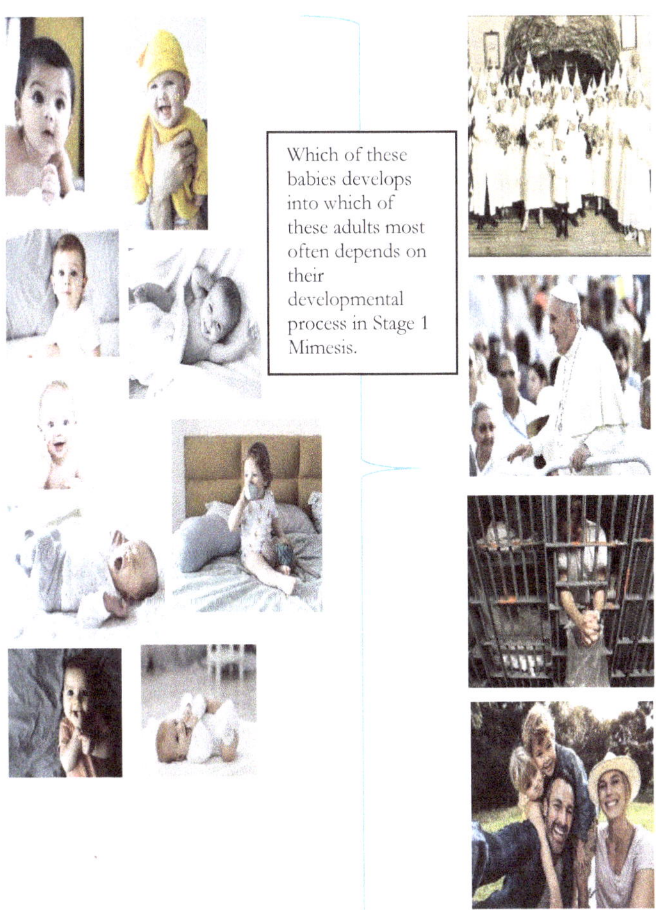

The early stages of human development are critical to the formation of an individual's thinking and direction in their life. Life Experience and how the individual is conditioned to respond to the experiences they encounter are what further develop an individual's cognitive perspectives and thinking. The early phase of Stage 2 is a continuation of the Stage 1 learning. An individual's personality stabilization does not occur until middle adulthood. Personality consistencies become noticeable during childhood. According to research published in the Journal of Psychology and Aging, lifelong personality stability has not previously been assessed; however, existing evidence of personality stability takes place from childhood (14 years old) to middle-late adulthood (30), and from early middle adulthood to older age suggests that personality stabilization is a process that takes place across the entire life course.[33] The way a person thinks determines how they behave. The personality stabilization process suggests that a person can respond to phenomena or ideologies differently at different periods in their life evolution. What is the difference between a student who gets good grades and a student who gets mediocre or bad grades? What is the difference between a person who makes a lot of money and a person who barely survives? What is the difference between people who stay married for life and people who get divorced? What is the difference in a person's thinking who smokes or uses drugs at 14 -20, then stops smoking and using drugs at age 30? What is the difference in a person's thinking who is raised in church during their youth (ages 10-18) by religious parents, then disconnects from religion when they go to college or become 21 years old? In short, what is the difference between one individual's life experiences and how they respond to phenomena they encounter, and the way another individual experiences life, and responds to the phenomena they encounter? What is the difference between an individual's thinking and behavior during different stages of their life? When different individuals live in the same environment (siblings, for example) or when siblings live in different environments, what factors cause different lives to experience different levels of satisfaction, success, or response from society? These are questions and issues that have roots in the life experiences individuals encounter, and the influences they encounter early in life (Stage 1 Mimesis) and throughout their lives (Stage 2 Mimesis). Coupling the decisions individuals make regarding the phenomena they encounter accounts for differences. The construction of an individual's Mimesis is formulated based on their response to lived experiences, emplotments, and phenomena encountered throughout their life.[3]

> Emplotment (countable and uncountable, plural emplotments) (historiography) is the assembly of a series of historical events (Lived Experiences) into a narrative with a plot. In the case of an individual, emplotment(s) are the basis for understanding an individual, and for making judgments about their character and personality.

Stage 2 Mimesis is where lived experiences are accumulated (creating emplotments). In Stage 2, the individual takes control over their choices, the phenomena they experience, and their behavior. Stage 2 Mimesis contains the emplotments[4] that create the narrative of an individual's life. Stage 2 involves rules that describe and interpret the behavior and actions of an individual. For example, running a red traffic light and you will get a ticket if you get caught. Make a habit of running red lights,

---

[3] **Emplotment Definition**
The assembly of a series of historical events in an individual's lifetime combines into a narrative with a plot that represents the reality of an individual's life.

and sooner or later, you will get caught. The red light is a symbol to "Stop". The green light is a symbol to "Go." A yellow light is a symbol to "Slow down. Exercise caution". In general, if an individual has a preunderstanding of the symbols in life and the behaviors that construct a life direction that aligns with the established rules of an orderly society, then the individual will encounter positive opportunities by displaying acceptable behaviors. This will give others a positive response to an individual. This behavior and response to the behavior feed the individual's narrative and put them in a position to write their own narrative. Having a preunderstanding, the individual can, to some extent, select the emplotments they engage and the narrative of their life. This gives individuals agency to construct their Mimesis. A significant characteristic of individuals in society is that many are reactive instead of proactive. Aforethought gives individuals the opportunity to be proactive with the phenomena they encounter and how they respond to them. That is the advantage embedded in understanding the *"Three-Fold Mimesis of Life"*.

It is said that the best predictor of the future is the lived experiences and phenomena an individual encounters in the past and present. Considering human behavior, people on a positive life track can continue to have a positive life. People on a negative life track can continue to have a dysfunctional life, unless they encounter and respond positively to phenomena that change their life trajectory. People on a positive life track can have experiences that cause them to change and go on a dysfunctional life track. People on a dysfunctional life track can have experiences that cause them to change and take them on a positive life trajectory. Past lived experiences do not have to be a predictor of future phenomena. Lived experiences occurring in the present can be constructed to set direction for the future.

The future can be predetermined, based on the phenomena individuals encounter and construct in their present lived experiences. The exercise of aforethought before an individual acts in response to phenomena they confront allows them to construct their Mimesis.

## Childhood Attachments Affect Adult Relationships

Caregiver, parental, friendships, relatives, teacher, or mentor relationships in the formative years of a child can mold and shape the way the child will experience relationships throughout their lives. How children relate and experience relationships in their early developmental years teaches them how to connect with others as they experience the various stages of growth in life. Children are more likely to model their own behavior after parents or caregivers who give them the experience of secure attachments. Likewise, children who experience traumatic attachments (Attachment Trauma) are more likely to develop personality disorders such as Borderline Personality Disorder (BPD), anxiety, stress, depression, distrust, and other trauma-related symptoms. Normally, the caregiver's influence on the child reflects the experience the caregiver themselves have had. Attachment Trauma is:[34]

> *"**Attachment Trauma** is defined as any event that happens to us that is severely emotionally distressing and falls outside of our natural resiliency and natural abilities to cope. When trauma is based on attachment, this suggests a rupture in the parent/child bonding process during the formative years that is not repaired but is perpetuated from one attachment wound to another."*

Attachment Trauma is associated with caregivers of parents who are negligent, abusive, emotionally unavailable or abandoning.

> *"When there is a secure base between caregiver and child, a rupture in attachment is typically met with repair and correction. This can become a teaching moment for both the parent and the child."*[35]

Attachment trauma that is not corrected, according to Dr. Tanasugarn, leaves the child feeling *"confused, angry, neglected, and abandoned. In time, and without support, the child's sense of self-identity can be compromised, which often predisposes them to similar patterns of trauma in their adult intimate relationships".* [36]

Attachment Theory is a concept developed by John Bowlby and Mary Ainsworth. It is discussed in more detail in a subsequent section of this chapter. In the context of *"Psychological Theories of Development"*, attachments in the early stages of development are relevant to each of the Developmental Theories. The developmental process determining an individual's migration through *the Mimesis of Life* is a complicated and complex process. It involves numerous phenomena that the individual will encounter. How the individual responds to the phenomena they encounter is affected by the early childhood development process mentioned by the various psychologists in the following section. Their early childhood attachments are factors in each of the following developmental theories. Each of the early childhood theories mentioned is relevant to the personality formation of an individual. In addition, early childhood attachment integrates with each theory and impacts each of the Theories of Development.

## Psychological Theories of Development that Influence the Three-Fold Mimesis of Life

There are several psychologists who have advanced theories on the developmental process from early childhood, through adolescence, through early adulthood, to senior adulthood. Development theories explain how individuals develop, change, and grow over the course of their childhood through life. Development theories focus on social, emotional, and cognitive growth. Human development, especially in the infant stages, can determine the lived experiences individuals encounter, the life choices they make, and how they behave during stages of their life cycle. Developmental theories address, explain, and predict behaviors that occur throughout an individual's life. To understand human development, several different theories of child, adolescent, and adult development exist to explain various aspects of human behavior. Caregivers, parents, or guardians determine what the infant experiences, from birth to preschool (3-6 years). In the early stages of adolescence, an individual begins to determine for themselves some of the lived experiences they encounter; they begin to make life choices that impact how they behave during this stage of their life cycle and possibly throughout. Choices the adolescent makes can either be reinforced based on additional life experiences or changed based on subsequent life experiences and decisions. Developmental theories address, explain, and predict behaviors that occur throughout an individual's life. To understand human development, several different theories of child development exist to explain various aspects of human behavior.

A significant and far more insidious and widespread impact on a child's life is based on the positive or negative experiences in their formative years (birth to 8 years). Among the most significant forms of negative experience is deprivation (the damaging lack of socialization and development benefits from the primary caregiver or parents, considered to be basic to functionality in society). Deprivation affects millions of children around the world who experience psychological neglect early in life—for example, children who are neglected by their families numbered greater than 500,000 in the US alone in 2013. [37] Human infants are born requiring the care and support of adult caregivers for survival. An essential role of parenting in the earliest years of life is providing regulation that molds the developing immature infant. Through reading (becoming basically informed on child development and psychology) and responding to infant behavioral cues, caregivers provide essential input necessary for the proper elaboration of essential domains of development, such as stress response systems, attentional systems, and attachment. The early stages of development mold the brain function of an individual and give a foundation for the behavioral function in the future years into adulthood.[38] At birth, the individual is subject to the environment they are born into. They inherit genetic characteristics of their birth parents. At birth, at the point of individual consciousness, is where Mimesis begins.

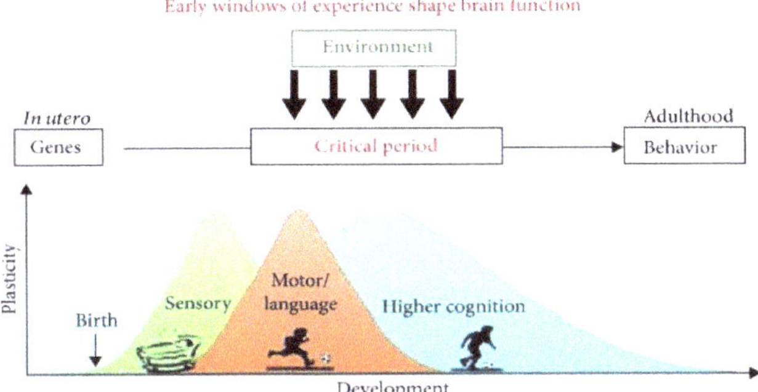


## Psychology Theories of Development

This section reviews the development theories of a renowned psychologist. These psychologists were selected because each has a different theory on the developmental process. The human development process is a complex phenomenon that involves multiple factors. Each of the theories these psychologists advance is relevant to the developmental process, with no one theory describing the entirety of development. The life cycle developmental process of an individual involves the theories described by each of the following theories.

### Psychosexual Theory of Human Development

Sigmund Freud, Austrian psychiatrist, psychologist, psychoanalyst, and neurologist (1856-1939).

### Cognitive Development Theory

Jean Piaget, Swiss psychologist (1896-1980)

### Social Learning Theory / Social Cognitive Theory

Albert Bandura, American-Canadian psychologist (1925-Present)

### Attachment Theory
John Bowlby, British psychologist (1907-1990)
Mary Ainsworth, psychologist (1913-1999)

### Psychosocial Developmental Theory
Erik Erikson, American-German psychologist (1902-1994)

### Sociocultural Theory
Lev Vygotsky's (1896 - 1934)

## Sigmund Freud (1856-1939) – Psychosexual Theory of Human Development

A pioneer in theories of human development is Sigmund Freud. [39] Freud related the development cycle of humans in their early stages to a concept of five Psychosexual Stages of human development. Stage 1 is The Oral Stage (Birth to 1 year old). The infant's primary source of interaction occurs through the mouth, and trust is established through the infant's dependence on being fed by the caregiver, normally the parents. The critical Stage during this stage is in the weaning process, training the child to become less dependent on the adult. If this stage does not transition in a smooth and positive manner, Freud concludes the child will have problems with dependency or aggression, resulting in potential problems with drinking, eating disorders, smoking, or nail-biting.

Stage 2 is The Anal Stage (ages 1–3 years old). Stage 2 involves toilet training and the child learning to control their bowel and bladder functions. Freud believed that positive training at this stage creates the foundation for the child to become competent, productive, and creative. Failure by caregivers to manage this stage properly causes the individual to have a messy, wasteful, or destructive personality. A caregiver who is too strict at this stage can result in the child developing stringent, orderly, rigid, and obsessive personality traits.

Stage 3 is the Phallic Stage (ages 3-6 years old). Freud suggests that the focus of stage 3 is on the libido and the genitals, and children discover the differences between males and females. Characteristic of this stage, according to Freud, is that boys compete with the father for the mother's attention, and likewise, girls compete with the mother for the attention of the father. Proper guidance during this stage aligns the relationship between mother/son, father/daughter into a proper perspective for the child. Inadequate guidance at this stage can result in role and gender confusion, according to Freud.

Stage 4 is the Latent Period (ages 6 to Puberty). During this stage, the superego (the part of a person's mind that acts as a self-critical conscience, reflecting social standards learned from parents and teachers) continues to develop while the id's (the part of the mind in which innate instinctive impulses, primary processes, and self-centered instincts are manifest) are suppressed. Children develop social skills, values, and relationships with peers and adults outside of the family. During this period, the ego (a person's sense of self-esteem or self-importance) is developed to contribute to the balance in their life. Individuals explore and experience adolescent interests. This stage is important in the development of social and communication skills and self-confidence. Complications at this stage can result in immaturity and an inability to form fulfilling relationships as an adult.

Stage 5 is the Genital Stage, which Freud contends lasts from puberty until death.

During this final stage of development, as puberty develops, the libido becomes active. Interest in the opposite sex and sexual desires emerge. This stage, according to Freud, lasts until death. The objective of this stage is to establish a balance between the various areas of life and to align a consistency in the lived experiences individuals encounter. Assuming the previous stages of Freud's development theory were accomplished successfully the individual should become well-balanced, warm, and caring. Teenagers who develop with a positive balance throughout the five stages should be able to align their personal and selfish interests with the social norms of society and reality, according to Freud.

Freud's development theory is not without opposition. Freud's theory is based significantly on psychological sexuality. The following theories give other viewpoints on human development based on different research methods and different periods in time. It is thought that during Freud's era (1856-1939), the social norm of society was to suppress individual sexuality. Possibly, Freud's research uncovered the repression of this basic human instinct as a component of the human development process during his era. Another consideration is that during Freud's era, the dynamics of society had changed. Developmental theories are also reflective of the times and environment in which people live. Just as times change, so do the needs of people. However, in today's society, there is still a lot of misalignment in the perspectives on sexuality. Some people think LGBTQ individuals are abnormal. Others believe LGBTQ individuals are human beings with human rights to be honored. Some people think an individual's sexual orientation is a factor of their developmental and socialization process. LGBTQ perspectives are oriented likewise to racist ideologies, viewpoints, and perspectives. Some humans have an inability to relate positively to individuals who hold different beliefs, a different orientation, and who have religious or color differences, even when the different individuals are "good" people. It is a sickness in American society, a society that is made up of diverse people, cultures, ideologies, perspectives, and viewpoints. Racism and discrimination are a sickness in American society. The same ideologies existed in Freud's era. The fact that people hold abnormal beliefs about sexual phenomena that are natural and normal is an example of ignorance.

## Albert Bandura (1925-Present) - Social Learning Theory / Social Cognitive Theory

The Social learning theory developed by psychologist Albert Bandura advanced that the conditioning and reinforcement process alone does not sufficiently explain the totality of human learning or the human learning process. Bandura believed learned behaviors are learned by classical conditioning or operant conditioning methods. "Classical conditioning[5] is a learning process that occurs when two stimuli are repeatedly paired: a response that is at first elicited by the second stimulus is eventually elicited by the first stimulus alone. Operant conditioning,[6] sometimes referred to as instrumental conditioning, it is a method of learning that employs rewards and punishments for behavior.

[5] **Classical conditioning theory** states that behaviors are learned by connecting a neutral stimulus with a positive one, such as Pavlov's dogs hearing a bell (neutral) and expecting food (positive). The learned behavior is called a conditioned response.

[6] **Operant conditioning**, sometimes referred to as instrumental conditioning, is a method of learning that uses rewards and punishment to modify behavior. Through operant conditioning, behavior that is rewarded is likely to be repeated, and behavior that is punished will rarely occur.

Through operant conditioning, an association is made between a behavior and a consequence (whether negative or positive) for that behavior." Behaviors can also be learned through observation and modeling, according to Bandura. Observing others causes children to develop new skills and information.[40] For example, a child learns to walk by observing others and by being coaxed by caregivers. Bandura's social learning theory advances that learning can occur by observing the behavior and actions of others.[41]

Bandura's social learning Theory was renamed Bandura's Cognitive Behavior Theory. The theory simply states; "human functioning emphasizes the critical role of self-beliefs in human cognition, motivation, and behavior. Social cognitive theory gives prominence to a self-system that enables individuals to exercise a measure of control over their thoughts, feelings, and actions". [42]

## The central concepts of social learning theory are: [43]

1) People can learn through observation.
2) Internal mental states are an essential part of this process.
3) Just because something has been learned, it does not mean that it will result in a behavior change.

Another concept advanced by Albert Bandura's social learning theory is self-efficacy. Self-efficacy is "the belief in one's capabilities to organize and execute the courses of action required to manage prospective situations. Self-efficacy[7] is a person's belief in his or her ability to succeed in a particular situation." Self-efficacy is about having a strong, positive belief that you have the capacity and the skills to achieve your goals.[44]

[7] Self-efficacy refers to an individual's belief in his or her capacity to execute behaviors necessary to produce specific performance attainments (Bandura, 1977, 1986, 1997). Self-efficacy reflects confidence in the ability to exert control over one's own motivation, behavior, and social environment.

It is important for an individual to be in the right mental state for learning to take place. Bandura recognized that external, environmental (extrinsic reinforcement) reinforcement was one factor that influences learning and behavior. He also realized that reinforcement does not always come from outside the individual's consciousness. An individual's mental state and motivation play an important role in determining whether a behavior is learned or not. Intrinsic reinforcement is an internal motivation that facilitates learning, resulting in gratification, pride, satisfaction, and a sense of accomplishment. Intrinsic reinforcement provides a connection between learning theories to cognitive developmental theories. Intrinsic motivation refers to behavior that is driven by internal rewards. In other words, the motivation to engage in a behavior arises from within the individual because it is naturally satisfying to you. This contrasts with extrinsic motivation, which involves engaging in a behavior in order to earn external rewards or avoid punishment. "Intrinsic motivation occurs when we act without any obvious external rewards. We simply enjoy an activity or see it as an opportunity to explore, learn, and actualize our potentials." 45

## John Bowlby (1907-1990) and Mary Ainsworth (1913-1999) - Attachment Theory

Normally, infants tend to develop attachment to their caregivers by 7 to 9 postnatal months. In conditions of neglect or deprivation, infants may fail to develop attachments to their caregivers. *"Early patterns of interaction between infants and parents are predictive of subsequent qualitative differences of attachment between them, and characteristics of parents assessed prenatally have been shown to predict individual differences in the quality of attachment between infants and parents more than one year later.*" The process of developing attachment in the infant stages can cause difficulty in human attachments and relationships later in life and throughout life. [46]

Attachment theory was developed by John Bowlby, a British child psychiatrist and psychoanalyst, in collaboration with Mary Ainsworth, an American psychoanalyst who studied infant/mother attachment patterns. The basis of Attachment Theory is that the parents or primary caregivers are available and responsive to an infant's needs. They support the child to enable the development of a feeling of security within the child. The infant is securely aware of the caregiver's dependability. This creates a secure foundation for the child, allowing them to freely explore their environment. [47] Bowlby advanced that early relationships with caregivers play a major role in child development and continue to influence social relationships throughout life.

*"Bowlby's attachment theory suggested that children are born with an innate need to form attachments. Such attachments aid in survival by ensuring that the child receives care and protection. Not only that, but these attachments are characterized by clear behavioral and motivational patterns. Both children and caregivers engage in behaviors designed to ensure proximity.*

*Children strive to stay close and connected to their caregivers who in turn provide safety and a secure base for exploration. Children who receive consistent support and care are more likely to develop a secure attachment style, while those who receive less reliable care may develop an ambivalent, avoidant, or disorganized style."* [48]

Mary Ainsworth elaborated on Bowlby's research on attachment and developed an approach to observing a child's attachment to a caregiver. Based on her research, she identified three major styles of attachment that children have to their parents or caregivers.

*All attachments that occur through Life cannot be blamed on parents or caregivers. At some point during an individual's life cycle, they must take responsibility for their behavior.*

Attachment styles formed during early childhood are not necessarily identical to those demonstrated in adult romantic attachments or attachments with other adults during adulthood. However, early attachment styles *can* help predict patterns of behavior in adulthood.

The time that elapses from childhood to adulthood involves numerous lived experiences that can influence an individual's behavior. Experiences that occur in the adult stages of life play a significant role in adult attachment styles. That creates the potential for individuals who have a dysfunctional childhood to change the relationships they have with people and the relationship they have with themselves. Because the environment is also a significant factor in socialization, a change in attachment relationships may also require a change in an individual's environment. Research indicates that the best predictor of adult attachment style was the perceptions people have about the quality of their relationships with their parents and their parents' relationship with each other. [49]

## Secure Attachments have the following Characteristics: [50]

- Children who are securely attached generally become visibly upset when their caregivers leave and are happy when their parents return.

- Children who are securely attached greet the return of a parent with positive behavior.

- When frightened, children will seek comfort from the parent or caregiver.

- Contact initiated by a parent is readily accepted by securely attached children

- While these children can be comforted to some extent by other people in the absence of a parent or caregiver, they clearly prefer parents to strangers.

- Parents of securely attached children tend to play more with their children.

- Parents react more quickly to their children's needs

- Parents are generally more responsive to their children than the parents of insecurely attached children.

- Securely attached children are more empathetic during later stages of childhood.

- Securely attached children are also described as less disruptive, less aggressive, and more mature than children with ambivalent or avoidant attachment styles.

**As adults, those who are securely attached have the following Characteristics:**

- Tend to have to trust long-term relationships.

- Tend to have high self-esteem,

- Enjoying intimate relationships

- Seek out social support and have the ability to share feelings with other people.

"Mothers who are not consistent in responding to the child's needs or who interfere with a child's activities tend to produce infants who explore less, cry more, and are more anxious. Mothers who consistently reject or ignore their infant's needs tend to produce children who try to avoid contact." [51]

## _The three major styles of attachment_

_Ambivalent Attachment_

_Avoidant Attachment_

_Disorganized Attachment_

**Ambivalent Attachment** is the least common of the attachment styles. [52]

- Children who are ambivalently attached tend to be extremely suspicious of strangers. These children display considerable distress when separated from a parent or caregiver,

- Ironically, they do not seem reassured or comforted by the return of the parent.

- In some cases, the child might passively reject the parent by refusing comfort, or may openly display direct aggression toward the parent.

- Ambivalent attachment causes insecure attachment and is linked to low maternal availability. As these children grow older, teachers often describe them as clingy and over-dependent.

As Adults, individuals who experience **Ambivalent Attachment are:**

- Reluctant to become close to others.

- Worry that their partner does not love them.

- Become very distraught when relationships end.

- As adults, we often cling to young children as a source of security.


## Avoidant Attachment Characteristics [53]

Children who experience avoidant attachment tend to avoid parents and caregivers. This avoidance often becomes especially pronounced after a period of absence. While children who experience avoidant attachment may not reject attention from a parent, they may not actively seek parental attention or contact. Children with an avoidant attachment seem to have no preference between a parent and a stranger.

As Adults

- Children who experience avoidant attachment may have problems with intimacy.

- Children who experience avoidant attachment invest lack emotion in social and romantic relationships and are more likely to engage in casual sex.

- Children who experience avoidant attachment are unwilling or unable to share thoughts or feelings with others and unsupportive of partners during stressful times.

## Disorganized Attachment Characteristics [54]

Children who experience disorganized-insecure attachment display a lack of clear attachment behavior. Their actions and responses to caregivers are often a mix of behaviors, including avoidance or resistance. These children are described as displaying dazed behavior, sometimes seeming either confused or apprehensive in the presence of a caregiver. Children who experience disorganized-insecure attachment may take on a parental role, acting as a caregiver toward the parent. Parental inconsistency may also be a contributing factor in Disorganized Attachment. Parents who have an inconsistent behavior pattern toward children, as figures of both fear and reassurance, create confusion in the child. Individuals who do not make positive attachments in their developmental years may lack in the development of their cognitive and social behavior. Studies suggest that the older a child becomes without any positive attachment (especially kids who have lived in an institution), the lower the child's IQ and the poorer the child is regarding their adaptive behavior. [55]

## <u>Erik Erikson (1902-1994) - <u>Psychosocial Developmental Theory</u></u>

Erikson's theory describes the effect of social experience across the whole lifespan. Erikson was interested in how social interaction and relationships played a role in the development and growth of human beings. Erikson's advances a psychosocial eight-stage theory of development describing growth and change throughout life. His focus is on social interaction and conflicts that arise during different stages of development. Central to Erikson's theory is the role of social interaction and lived experience being important to the developmental process. Erikson's eight-stage theory of human development describes the development process from infancy through death. In each stage of development, individuals are confronted with developmental conflicts that impact later functioning and subsequent growth. Erikson's psychosocial theory focuses on development across the entire lifespan. At each stage, children and adults face a developmental crisis that serves as a critical path in their lived experience. Successfully managing the challenges of each stage results in positive and satisfying lived experiences and a functional life.[56]

| Psychosocial Stages: A Summary Chart [57] | | | |
|---|---|---|---|
| **Age** | **Conflict** | **Important Events** | **Outcome** |
| <u>**Stage 1 Mimesis**</u> | | | |
| **Infancy** (birth to 18 months) | Trust vs. Mistrust | Feeding | Hope |
| **Early Childhood** (2 to 3 years) | Autonomy vs. Shame and Doubt | Toilet Training | Will |
| **Preschool** (3 to 5 years) | Initiative vs. Guilt | Exploration | Purpose |
| <u>**Stage 2 Mimesis**</u> | | | |
| **School Age** (6 to 11 years) | Industry vs. Inferiority | School | Confidence |
| **Adolescence** (12 to 18 years) | Identity vs. Role Confusion | Social Relationships | Fidelity |
| **Young Adulthood** (19 to 40 years) | Intimacy vs. Isolation | Relationships | Love |
| **Middle Adulthood** (40 to 65 years) | Generativity vs. Stagnation | Work and Parenthood | Care |
| <u>**Stage 3 Mimesis**</u> | | | |
| **Maturity** (65 to death) | Ego Integrity vs. Despair | Reflection on Life | Wisdom |

## Erickson's Psychosocial Developmental Theory

### Stage 1: Trust vs. Mistrust (Birth - 1 year old) [58] Mimesis Stage 1

The first stage of Erikson's theory of psychosocial development is the most critical stage in life, because an infant is dependent. Developing trust is based on the dependability and quality of the child's parents or caregivers. If a caregiver fails to provide food, love, warmth, safety, and nurturing, the child will come to feel that they cannot trust or depend upon the adults in their life.

### Outcomes

A child who successfully develops trust will feel safe and secure in the world. Caregivers who are inconsistent, emotionally unavailable, or rejecting contribute to feelings of mistrust in the children under their care. Failure to develop trust will result in fear and a belief that the world is inconsistent and unpredictable. Erikson believed that successful development was all about striking a balance between the two opposing sides. A positive balance establishes hope, which Erikson believes gives the child an openness to explore and experience their environment, while being weary and cautious of dangers that may be present.

## Psychosocial Developmental Theory

### Stage 2: Autonomy vs. Shame and Doubt (Early Childhood) Mimesis Stage 1

The second stage of Erikson's theory of psychosocial development is focused on children developing a greater sense of personal control. At this development stage, children are starting to experience some independence, independently performing basic actions and making simple decisions about what they want. When parents allowing kids to make choices and gain control, children develop a sense of autonomy.

The characteristic of this stage is that children need to develop control over their physical skills which contributes to their sense of independence. Training to exercise control over their bowel and urine functions (potty training) is critical in helping children develop a sense of autonomy. In common with Freud, Erikson believed that toilet training was a critical part of developing a child's independence. However, Erikson's reasoned that learning to control one's bodily functions leads to a feeling of control and a sense of independence. Gaining an independence carries forward to the child exercising control in other areas of their life; food choices, toy preferences, and clothing selections.

## Outcomes

Children who struggle with this stage of development and who feel shame if they have accidents, may become insecure and feel a lack of personal control. Success during this stage of psychosocial development leads to feelings of autonomy; failure results in feelings of shame and doubt. Children who successfully complete this stage feel secure and confident, while those who do not are left with a sense of inadequacy and self-doubt. "Erikson believed that achieving a balance between autonomy and shame and doubt would lead to will, which is the belief that children can act with intention, within reason and limits." [59]

## Stage 3: Initiative vs. Guilt (Preschool Years)

## Psychosocial Developmental Theory

### Stage 3: Initiative vs. Guilt (Preschool) Mimesis Stage 2

In the third stage of psychosocial development children begin to assert their power and control over the world through directing play and other social interactions.

Children who are successful at this stage feel capable and able to lead others. Those who fail to acquire these skills are left with a sense of guilt, self-doubt, and lack of initiative.

## Outcomes

The major theme of the third stage of psychosocial development is that children who successfully engage this stage of development begin to assert their control and power over the environment. Success in this stage leads to a sense of purpose. Children who try to exert too much power experience disapproval, resulting in a sense of guilt. When an ideal balance of individual initiative and a willingness to work with others is achieved, the ego and a sense of purpose emerge. [60]

## Psychosocial Developmental Theory

### Stage 4: Industry vs. Inferiority (Ages 5-11) Mimesis Stage 2

In the fourth psychosocial, through social interactions, children begin to develop a sense of pride in their accomplishments and abilities. Children should learn to cope with new social and academic experiences. Success leads to a sense of competence, while failure results in feelings of inferiority.

## Outcomes

Children who are encouraged and positively reinforced by parents and teachers develop a sense of competence and belief in their skills. Those who receive little or no encouragement from parents, teachers, or peers will doubt their abilities to be successful. Successfully finding a balance at this stage of psychosocial development leads to competence and children develop confidence in their ability to handle the tasks and situations that confront them.[61]

## Psychosocial Developmental Theory

### Stage 5: Identity vs. Confusion (Teenage years)
### Mimesis Stage 2

The fifth psychosocial stage is often a challenging time in the teenage years. This stage is critical in developing a sense of personal identity, which will continue to influence behavior and development for the rest of a person's life. Teens need to develop a sense of self and personal identity. Success leads to self-confidence and a healthy self-image, aligned with the individual's environment. Failure leads to role confusion and a weak sense of self. During adolescence, children explore their independence and develop a sense of self. Those who receive proper encouragement and reinforcement through personal exploration will develop self-confidence, a sense of independence, and control. Those who are unsure of themselves will feel insecure and confused about their present and their future. Life experiences in this stage of development can have a long-term impact on an individual's life.

When psychologists talk about identity, they are referring to all beliefs, ideals, and values that shape and guide a person's behavior. Completing this stage successfully leads to fidelity, which Erikson described as the ability to live by society's standards and expectations. Self-identity defines that integrated and cohesive sense of self that endures through our lives. Our sense of personal identity is influenced by our life experiences and interactions with others. It influences our actions, beliefs, and behaviors as we age.

Erikson placed an emphasis on the development of an individual's ego identity.

*"Ego identity is the conscious sense of self that we develop through social interaction and becomes a central focus during the identity versus confusion stage of psychosocial development. Our ego identity constantly*

*changes due to new experiences and information we acquire in our daily interactions with others. As we have new experiences, we also take on challenges that can help or hinder the development of identity.* [62]

## Psychosocial Developmental Theory

## Stage 6: Intimacy vs. Isolation (Early adult) Mimesis Stage 2

During this stage, young adults form intimate, loving relationships with other people. Success leads to strong relationships, while failure results in loneliness and isolation. During this stage, people explore personal relationships. Developing close, committed relationships with other people is critical for life balance at this stage. People who are successful at this step will form relationships that are lasting and secure. Each stage in the psychosocial development process builds on skills learned in prior stages. A secure and stable understanding of one's personal identity is important for developing intimate relationships. Individuals with a poor self-identity tend to have less committed relationships and are subject to experiencing difficulty with emotional isolation, loneliness, and depression. Successfully reconciling this stage allows the individual to be open to intimacy and loving relationships. The ability to form lasting, meaningful relationships with other people is more likely. [63]

## Psychosocial Developmental Theory

## Stage 7: Generativity vs. Stagnation - Mimesis Stage 2

Successful-minded adults need to create a legacy. Having children or creating a positive change that benefits other people are methods to accomplish this. Success leads to feelings of usefulness and accomplishment, while failure results in shallow involvement in the world. During adulthood, individuals engage ongoing effort to construct their lives, focusing on career and family. Successful participation during this phase makes adults feel they are contributing to their environment by being active in their home and community. Those who fail to attain this achievement may feel unproductive and uninvolved in their environment and community. Care is a result of achievement in. Being proud of your accomplishments, watching your children grow into adults, and developing a sense of unity with your life partner are important accomplishments of this stage. [64]

## Psychosocial Developmental Theory

## Stage 8: Integrity vs. Despair (Senior – Old Age) Mimesis Stage 3

The final psychosocial stage is focused on reflecting back on life. At this point in development, people look back on the events of their lives and determine if they are happy with the life that they lived or if they regret the things they did or didn't do. Erikson's theory is different from the others because it addresses development throughout the entire lifespan, including old age. Older adults need to look back on life and feel a sense of fulfillment. Success at this stage leads to feelings of wisdom, while failure results in regret, bitterness, and despair. At this stage, people reflect on the events of their lives and take stock. Those who look back on a life they feel was well-lived will feel satisfied and ready to face the end of their lives with a sense of peace. Those who look back and only feel regret will instead feel fearful that their lives will end without accomplishment.

## Outcomes

Those who are unsuccessful during this stage will feel that their life has been wasted and may experience many regrets. The person may feel bitterness and despair. Those who are satisfied and proud of their accomplishments will have a sense of integrity. Successfully completing this phase means looking back with few regrets and a general feeling of satisfaction. These individuals will experience less anxiety and fear, even when confronting the process of dying and death. [65]

## Jean Piaget (1896-1980) - Cognitive Development Theory

Jean Piaget is a psychologist who advanced the Cognitive Development Theory. Piaget's Cognitive Development theory is based on a person's thought processes and how the thought processes influence the way individuals understand and interact with the world. Piaget's Cognitive Development Theory is based on four stages of how the mental state of an individual influences their thinking and how they interact with their environment. Piaget believed that children take an active role in the learning process. They are experimental, making observations as they learn about their environment. Children accumulate knowledge continuously, building on previous knowledge. Piaget advances four stages that account for the development of an individual's intellectual development. [66]

### "Sensorimotor Stage:

A period of time between birth and age two during which an infant's knowledge of the world is limited to his or her sensory perceptions and motor activities. Behaviors are limited to simple motor responses caused by sensory stimuli."[67]

In this first stage of cognitive development, infants and toddlers learn through sensory experiences and manipulating objects through basic reflexes, senses, and motor responses.

In this stage, children experience a period of considerable growth and learning. Interacting with their environment, everything they learn is new knowledge. Their learning about how the world works is constant.

The cognitive development occurring at this stage happens over a relatively short period of time, and growth is significant. Children learn physical activity, such as crawling and walking; they also learn about language from the people with whom they interact.

Piaget believed that at this stage, kids develop the understanding that objects exist even if they cannot be seen. By distinguishing objects as existing separate and distinct entities, children are able to start identifying objects, attaching names and words to objects.

## "Pre-Operational Stage:

A period between ages 2 and 6 during which a child learns to use language. During this stage, children do not yet understand concrete logic, cannot mentally manipulate information, and are unable to take the point of view of other people." [68]

The basics for language development are laid in the execution of language skills that emerge during the preoperational stage of development.

Children pretend play during this stage of development and continue to assimilate and organize the knowledge they absorb about their environment. Beginning to relate to others and develop consistencies and the ability to discriminate between objects happens at this stage.

## "Concrete Operational Stage:

A period between ages 7 and 11 during which children gain a better understanding of mental operations. Children begin thinking logically about concrete events but have difficulty understanding abstract or hypothetical concepts."[69]

At this stage, children still exist in a concrete material or physical form, not abstract. They are literal in their thinking, yet are becoming more skillful at using logic. The egocentrism of the previous stages dissipates, and kids begin to think about how other people perceive different situations.

Thinking becomes more logical during the concrete operational state; it can also be very rigid. Kids "at this point in development tend to struggle with abstract and hypothetical concepts."

Becoming less egocentric, kids begin to think about how other people might think and feel. Kids in the concrete operational stage also begin to understand that their thoughts are unique to them and that not everyone shares their thoughts, feelings, and opinions. Kids begin to understand the concept of individuality.

## "Formal Operational Stage:

A period between the ages of 12 to adulthood when people develop the ability to think about abstract concepts. Skills such as logical thought, deductive reasoning, and systematic planning also emerge during this stage." [70]

The final stage of Piaget's theory involves a growth in the individual's logic and ability to reason, the ability to use deductive reasoning, and an understanding of abstract ideas.

Individuals become capable of understanding multiple potential solutions to problems and think more scientifically about their environment.

The ability to think about abstract ideas and situations is an integral factor of the formal operational stage of cognitive development. The ability to logically think in terms of the future, project ahead, make plans, and reason about hypothetical situations develops during this stage.

Piaget perceived a child's mentality and intellectuality as a qualitative development process. The learning process is not just a quantitative building block process, of information and knowledge accumulation onto their existing knowledge with aging. Rather, Piaget advanced that there comes a point in cognitive development where the thinking process changes. The individual experiences a fundamental change in the way they think and reason about their environment. With aging and maturity, perspectives need and wants change. This is reflected in the lived experiences individuals encounter.

## <u>Lev Vygotsky's (1896 - 1934) - Sociocultural Theory</u>

Lev Semyonovich Vygotsky was a Soviet psychologist, best known for his work on psychological development in children and for creating the framework known as cultural-historical activity theory. Lev Vygotsky proposed a seminal learning theory that has gone on to become very influential, especially in the field of education. Like Piaget, Vygotsky believed that children learn actively and through hands-on experiences. Sociocultural theory, as an emerging theory in psychology, focuses on the influence society has on individual development. This theory has become more prominent in recent years. Sociocultural theory has application in the educational environment as well as in socialization and play. [71]

Vygotsky's sociocultural theory advances that parents, caregivers, peers,[72] and the culture at large are responsible for developing the higher-order functions in an individual. Vygotsky considers learning is a social process. By association and interaction with others, learning is facilitated by integrating lived experiences into the individual's understanding of the world.

Vygotsky's child development theory introduced the concept of the *"zone of proximal development*, which is the gap between what a person can do with help and what they can do on their own."* It is with the help of more knowledgeable others that people can progressively learn and increase their skills and scope of understanding. [73] Sociocultural theory advances that individuals are products of the life experiences they encounter in conjunction with the social interactions they encounter. According to sociocultural theory psychological growth is determined by the people in our lives, individuals who guide us, parents (are primary), mentors, teachers. Participation in social events (sports) and interactions with social groups (fraternities, debate club, gangs). The values an individual internalizes are a combination of their experiences gained from individuals who guide their life and interaction and participation in social groups. Another influence on an individual's life according to sociocultural theory is the cultural heritage of the individual. [74]

A crucial component in sociocultural theory is the *"Zone of Proximal Development."* The *Zone of Proximal Development* is defined by Vygotsky as "the distance between the actual development level of an individual and the level of potential development as determined through problem solving under adult guidance or collaboration with peers."

The skills, knowledge, and learning that an individual cannot acquire through social interaction but requires the guidance of others who are more skilled is the *Zone of Proximal Development*, according to sociocultural theory. [75]

|  | Piaget | Vygotsky |
| --- | --- | --- |
| Sociocultural context | Little emphasis | Strong emphasis |
| Constructivism | Cognitive constructivist | Social constructivist |
| Stages | Strong emphasis on stages of development | No general stages of development proposed |
| Key processes in development & learning | Equilibration; schema; adaptation; assimilation; accommodation | Zone of proximal development; scaffolding; language/dialogue; tools of the culture |
| Role of language | Minimal – Language provides labels for children's experiences (egocentric speech) | Major – Language plays a powerful role in shaping thought |
| Teaching implications | Support children to explore their world and discover knowledge | Establish opportunities for children to learn with the teacher and more skilled peers |

## The Critical Role of Social Referencing

Social referencing is critical in the life experience of a child who will be a primary agent in constructing their Mimesis. The parental and caregiver responsibility to build a foundation upon which the child develops their Mimesis. Social referencing plays a key role in a child's confidence level, their self-confidence, their self-efficacy. A parent who is conscious of the role of social referencing plays in the child's developmental process can give the child a foundation of well-being that will carry them through life.

An infant comes into the world as a blank slate. Everything they see and encounter is new. Their environment, people, and every situation, incident, phenomenon, and lived experience are all entities that feed an infant's learning process and are catalysts to their learning. The influence of social referencing in a child's developmental process cannot be overestimated. It is a critical component in the way a child engages in their world. For the child, social referencing is a primary method by which they learn to adapt to their new environment and their new condition, *consciousness*. **Social referencing** is the process by which infants learn to understand and respond to their environment based on and resulting from the affective interactions with an adult (parent or caregiver) to regulate their behaviors. Social referencing represents one of the major mechanisms by which infants come to understand the world. The child uses social referencing to understand and respond to their environmental objects, persons, and situations they encounter. [76]

Babies and infants learn to respond to the world and all they encounter based on how they interpret expressions, reactions and actions of individuals around them. Infants instinctively psychologically learn from actions and reactions of adult emotive responses. Infant behaviors, actions and reactions are formulated from their instinctive sense of what they interpret in adult behavior. "Social referencing is a vital tool that helps infants to get a sense of their new environment and the people and objects that form a part of it". [77]

Social referencing is closely related to attachment, the child's desire to be close to and acknowledged by their primary caregiver. This is especially clear when we think of social referencing in terms of the desire for emotional co-regulation, rather than information-seeking alone. Social referencing can be a critical factor in childhood validation and well-being. Considering that every experience the child encounters will be new, and give them some insight into their environment. [78]

**Social referencing** should teach the infant empathy, social competence, and is important in their emotional development. From parents and caregivers, infants learn to distinguish different emotions, sounds, expressions, and they learn how to relate to people and objects. Social referencing develops the ability in Infants to make decisions about what actions they need to take in certain situations. Social referencing lays the foundation for children to learn and develop socialization and decision-making skills, to can apply throughout their lives. Social referencing is a critical developmental tool; parents should be keenly aware of when they interact with the child.

## Childhood Validation and Development of Well-Being [79]

Validation is the act of understanding, recognizing, and giving value to an individual's needs, feelings, thoughts, emotions, and behavior as being important, having a valid presence. The provision of validation is based on being able to empathize with another person and relate to his or her reality based on his or her lived experiences.

Invalidation occurs when an individual suffers from beliefs that their needs, feelings, or lived emotional experiences are not important and do not matter. A lack of self-esteem develops when an individual is socialized in their childhood developmental process to believe that how they perceive their world and how they respond to that perception is unreasonable or insignificant. This perspective, imprinted in their minds, develops into and creates feelings of insecurity, an unsure self-identity, self-consciousness, depression, a lack of trust in themselves and in others. [80]

Some key concerns are:

- Emotional invalidation in childhood is linked to borderline personality disorder and pathological narcissism.

- Childhood invalidation can lead to later feelings of insecurity, deep depression, and an unstable sense of self-identity.

- Feeling unheard or unseen in childhood can lead to avoiding emotional intimacy or vulnerability in adulthood.

Some of the effects of invalidation in childhood that impact the individual in their adult years and result in adult dysfunction are:

- **Emotional Dysregulation** – "If a child routinely had their reality dismissed, minimized, or denied, they can struggle with identifying or expressing their emotions as an adult. They may become emotionally unavailable and can struggle to form or keep intimate relationships when emotional vulnerability is on the line".

- **Lack of Feeling Safe** - Relationships that are safe and affirming can help establish a solid foundation for trust and feeling validated. A person's ability to feel safe in their relationships is critical to their overall relational satisfaction. Not feeling safe can cause adults to be attracted to individuals who negatively reinforce their best interests.

If corrective intervention is absent from the child's early developmental process, then the cycle of dysfunction from Invalidation repeats itself in the way they interact with their children and in their intimate relationships. Patterns to recognize are:[81]

- Deep feelings of emptiness and feeling lonely, even when in a relationship

- Feeling unheard, unseen, or misunderstood

- Chronic feelings of guilt, shame, depression, or anxiety

- Miscommunication or a severing of communication (keeping communication shallow or superficial)

- Avoiding emotional intimacy or vulnerability

- Selfish or self-serving behaviors that may affect the other person

- Acting without thinking

- Inability to relate, empathize, or comfort the other person

- Emotional dysregulation (often vacillating between shutting down or lashing out)

- Feelings of Insecurity and inadequacy

Kids who develop with strong mental functionality have the following influences: [82]

1) Negativity is detected and eradicated before it becomes integral to a child's mindset.

2) Teach kids to reference with positive terminology. For example: terms such as "I can do this" or "I can figure this out" or "I understand this". Reference to their lived experiences that indicate their ability to grow and learn.

3) Teach kids not to avoid problems or challenges but to brainstorm and figure out solutions. Ask "what-if questions". Do possibility thinking.

4) The media is full of negative information. Make sure kids get an abundance of hopeful and positive news to out-balance the negative phenomena they will encounter.

5) Give positive feedback to small accomplishments and project the ability to improve. For example: "Wonderful, today you got 8 correct out of 12. Tomorrow you will get all 12 correct".

6) Reinforce the value of assertiveness to give the child a sense of standing up for themselves. For example: responses your child can use to assert themselves: "That's not right" or "I don't want to do that" or "That's not smart".

7) Develop a ritual of gratitude and thankfulness where the child shows appreciation to entities that make positive contributions to their lives.

8) Construct a kid's life experience to contribute acts of service to the community, the school, or others. Show and demonstrate the value of giving back.

With the right tools, kids will be able to handle adverse phenomena they encounter in their lived experience and be able to avoid hopelessness with feelings of hope and have a positive perspective toward life. Being hopeful feeds mental fortitude, happiness, and success. Kids who are hopeful are set apart from those who allow dysfunction to take over their lives.

Psychology research studies indicate that some of the benefits of a child or an individual experiencing a positive Stage 1 and Stage Mimesis are as follows: [83]

1) A positive Stage 1 Mimesis sets the stage for a positive Stage 2 Mimesis and gives the individual an advantage in achieving emotional balance, resilience to manage life's challenges and fluctuations, and fuels an individual's ability to avoid neuroticism in an emotionally intelligent manner without the characteristics of Stoicism.

2) The individual is better equipped to achieve equilibrium of the Mine

3) The individual is better equipped to develop mindfulness skills in the context of education as a means to improve psychological well-being, together with work-related skills and performance of children and adolescents, personally, socially, academically, and professionally.

4) Psychology research is responsible for the widespread acceptance of a 5 factor model that is a representation of an individual's personality structure. The five factors are *Neuroticism, Extraversion, Openness, Agreeableness, and Conscientiousness.* The consensus among psychology professionals is that a functional stage 2 Mimesis improves the individual's comprehensiveness, universality, and heritability factors, allows the individual to pass along positive characteristics to future generations, long-term functional stability, and the individual is better equipped to respond positively to their lived experiences and the phenomena they encounter. The validity of the 5 personality factors results as follows:

| Trait | Low Scorers | High Scorers |
| --- | --- | --- |
| **Openness** | Consistent | Inventive |
| | Or Cautious | Or Curious |
| **Conscientious** | Easy Going | Efficient |
| | Or Careless | Or Organized |
| **Extraversion** | Solitary | Outgoing |
| | Or Reserved | Or Energetic |
| **Agreeableness** | Analytical | Friendly |
| | Or Detached | Or Compassionate |
| **Neuroticism** | Secure | Sensitive |
| | Or Confident | Or Nervous |

## The Environment as a Determinant Factor in Mimesis Construction (Lived Experiences and Choices)

As indicated in the Developmental Theories, the environment plays a significant role in the lived experiences and phenomena people encounter, the decisions they are confronted with to make, and the individuals they interact with. Not everyone has the advantage of growing up in the middle-class or upper-class suburban areas of America. Many minorities grow up in urban areas where the propensity for dysfunction is stereotypically greater. Minorities have different lived experiences from Whites. A major reason for this is the variable factors in the environment, the White and Black differential. The responsiveness of society to the needs of each culture is also different. American society is more responsive to the needs of White people than it is to the needs of Black and minority people. This is no secret. It has been this way for centuries. Kids are exposed to a more dynamic lifestyle in the inner city. Many questionable opportunities and choices are combined with many good choices. This does not eliminate the fact that suburban dwellers are susceptible to dysfunction or that inner city dwellers have functional, positive, and happy lives. Challenges in life are a factor of being human. The suburbs have their share of dysfunction. This does not mean that all Black people live in urban areas and all Whites live in suburban areas. Frankly, life situations boil down to a number of circumstances: environmental circumstances, caregiver influence, the influence of associates, and the individual's lived experiences, and the choices people make in response to phenomena they encounter, whether the environmental setting is urban, suburban, or rural influenced.

## Breaking the Cycle of Dysfunction

The fact that there are so many individual differences in human beings indicates the dynamic differences and variability in the developmental processes of individuals. Just as the child can experience a functional and positive developmental process, the seeds of dysfunction can also be planted in the developmental process of the child. Many individuals encounter this phenomenon, and how they respond is equally as variable. The one thing to internalize is that there are many challenges in life and obstacles along the journey to a fulfilling life. If an individual experiences Attachment Trauma and they have dysfunction because of such trauma, it is important that they find ways to break the cycle of trauma so as not to pass it on to their kids. Therapy is one method of breaking the cycle of dysfunction. Attachment Trauma is a disadvantage, especially because a child carries this experience into their future. People encounter many handicaps. Some people are uneducated, some are over-educated, some are orphans, some are poor, some are gender redefined, some have problems dealing with gender redefinition, some are victims of racism, some are racists, some are victim of bullies, some are bullies, some are fat, some are short, some are too tall and some experience negative childhood attachments and trauma. Regardless of the handicap an individual experiences, they must find a way to overcome any trauma and personal insufficiency they perceive their handicap to cause. The truth is that everyone has something that challenges his or her self-esteem, his or her self-efficacy, and his or her confidence in life. The road to successful growth is found in the process of overcoming your real and your perceived social, personality, and behavioral trauma. One thing every individual should understand is that no one is perfect and everyone has an area of insecurity in their life (whether it is valid or not). All humans have an insecure "soft spot" that puts all people on an equal playing field in terms of dealing with themselves, dealing and with others. These human deficiencies are often a result of a lack of self-confidence, self-efficacy, and security. A double-edged commonality is that 1) some people only see inadequacy in themselves and do not realize everyone has problematic issues and 2) some people only see inadequacies in others and fail to realize the inadequacies in themselves.

# End Notes

---

1

The author describes the concept of being and non-being and the associated states of consciousness and the transcendental state of death in in more detail in his book: *"Everybody wants to Go to Heaven but nobody wants to Die"*. There are alternative viewpoints to the concept of *"Being and Non-Being"* based on cultural environments. This author focuses on the material Christian concept of being and non-being as the states of life and death.

"Being and non-being" explores the philosophical relationship between existence and non-existence, a fundamental question with different interpretations across various traditions, notably in Ancient Greek philosophy (e.g., Parmenides' focus on unchanging being vs. Plato's use of non-being to explain change) and Chinese philosophy (e.g., the concepts of you for existing and wu for emptiness). Buddhist philosophy also examines this dichotomy through the lens of impermanence and illusion, while concepts of being and non-being appear in Hindu, medieval, and contemporary thought".

Sadler, G. B. (2020). Parmenides of Elea | Being and Non-Being | Philosophy Core Concepts. *YouTube*. https://www.youtube.com/watch?v=8nAa7DOidq0&t=41s

Wang, Y., Bao, Q., Guan, G. (2020). Being and non-being (*youwu*, 有无). In: History of Chinese Philosophy Through Its Key Terms. Springer, Singapore. https://doi.org/10.1007/978-981-15-2572-8_15 .

https://link.springer.com/chapter/10.1007/978-981-15-25728_15#:~:text=Being%20(you)%20and%20non%2D,nothingness%20and%20not%20having%20form.

2

(Bartkowski, Acevedo & Van Loggerenberg, 2017; Jong, Bluemke & Halberstadt, 2013; Krause, 2015; Krause & Hayward, 2014; Van Tongeren, McIntosh, Raad & Pae, 2013)

Bartkowski, J. P., Acevedo, G. A., and Van Loggerenberg, H. (2017). Prayer, meditation, and anxiety: Durkheim Revisited. *Department of Sociology, The University of Texas at San Antonio, One UTSA Circle, San Antonio*. Retrieved from: https://www.mdpi.com/2077-1444/8/9/191/htm

Jong, J., Bluemke, M. and Halberstadt, J. (2014). Fear of death and supernatural beliefs: developing a new supernatural belief scale to test the relationship. *European Journal of Personality, Eur. J. Pers. (27), 495-506 (2013)*. DOI: 10.1002/per.1898. Retrieved from: https://onlinelibrary.wiley.com/doi/epdf/10.1002/per.1898

Krause, N. (2015). Trust in God, forgiveness by God, and death anxiety. *Omega: Journal of Death and Dying*, (72) 1, 20-41. doi:10.1177/0030222815574697. Retrieved from: https://lopes.idm.oclc.org/login?url=http://search.ebscohost.com/login.aspx?direct=true&db=edswss&AN=000365613600002&site=eds-live&scope=site

Krause, N., & Hayward, R. D. (2014). Religious involvement and death anxiety. *Omega: Journal of Death and Dying*, (69) *1, 59-78.*.doi:10.2190/OM.69.1.d. Retrieved from: http://journals.sagepub.com/doi/pdf/10.2190/OM.69.1.d

Krause, N., Pargament, K., I. and Ironson, G. (2016). In the shadow of death: religious hope as a moderator of the effects of age on death anxiety. *Journals of Gerontology, Psychol Sci Soc Sci, 2018, (73) 4, pp. 696–703.* doi:10.1093/geronb/gbw039. Retrieved from: https://academic.oup.com/psychsocgerontology/article/73/4/696/2632008

Krause, N. (2017). Religious involvement and self-forgiveness. *Mental Health, Religion & Culture*, (*20*) 2, 128–142. Retrieved from: https://doiorg.lopes.idm.oclc.org/10.1080/13674676.2017.1326477

3

Taylor, J. (2019). Perception is not reality. *Psychology Today.* https://www.psychologytoday.com/us/blog/the-power-prime/201908/perception-is-not-reality

4

Reality. BK101: Knowledge Base. Retrieved from: https://www.basicknowledge101.com/subjects/reality.html#:~:text=Reality%20are%20the%20things%20in,physically%20experienced%20by%20the%20senses.

5

Meyer, Josh (2022). Why are mass shooters getting younger and deadlier? Experts have theories. USA Today. Retrieved from: https://www.usatoday.com/story/news/politics/2022/07/07/mass-shooters-younger-deadlier/7813668001/?gnt-cfr=1 ;

https://www.usatoday.com/story/news/politics/2022/05/27/uvalde-attack-leaves-broken-lives-fractured-public-trust-police/9935204002/?gnt-cfr=1

6

Puetz, Michelle (2002). Mimesis. *University of Chicago.*
Retrieved from:
https://csmt.uchicago.edu/glossary2004/mimesis.htm

7

Swagatika, Kar (2021). What is the "Theory of Mimesis"?-
Aristotle Vs Plato. Retrieved from:
https://vocal.media/geeks/what-is-the-theory-of-mimesis

8

Juan-Navarro, Santiago. The Power of Mimesis and the
Mimesis of Power: Plato's concept of Imitation and his
Judgement on the Value of Poetry and the Arts. Retrieved
from: file:///C:/Users/Public/Dialnet-
ThePowerOfMimesisAndTheMimesisOfPower-
2542091.pdf

Philip, J. A. (1961). Mimesis in the Sophistês of
Plato. *Transactions and Proceedings of the American Philological
Association, 92,* 453–468. https://doi.org/10.2307/283830.
Retrieved from: https://www.jstor.org/stable/283830

9

Parasar, Bhaswati .The Theory of Mimesis. Rizvi College of
Arts, Science and Commerce. Retrieved from:
https://www.librarydrdl.com/pdf/econtent/Theory_of_M
imesis-BHASWATI.pdf

10

Common Ground (n.d.). Aristotle on Mimesis. Retrieved
from: http://neamathisi.com/new-learning/chapter-8-
pedagogy-and-curriculum/aristotle-on-mimesis

11

Baktir, Hassan, THE CONCEPT OF IMITATION IN
PLATO AND ARISTOTLE. Retrieved from:
https://dergipark.org.tr/tr/download/article-
file/219264#:~:text=Mimesis%2C%20as%20Aristotle%20t
akes%20it,into%20existence%20through%20'mimesis'.

12

English Veda. Mimesis? What is Mimesis? Plato and
Aristotle view on mimesis. Retrieved from:
https://www.englishveda.com/2020/04/mimesis-what-is-
mimesis-plato-and.html

Hasan BAKTIR.  THE CONCEPT OF IMITATION IN
PLATO AND ARISTOTLE. Retrieved from:
https://dergipark.org.tr/tr/download/article-file/219264

13

Plato (360 B.C.E.). The Republic, Book II. Translated by
Benjamin Jowett. Retrieved from:
http://classics.mit.edu/Plato/republic.3.ii.html

14

Puetz, M. (2002). Mimesis. University of Chicago, Theories
of Media. Retrieved from:
http://csmt.uchicago.edu/glossary2004/mimesis.htm

15

Puetz, M. (2002). Mimesis. University of Chicago, Theories
of Media. Retrieved from:
http://csmt.uchicago.edu/glossary2004/mimesis.htm

16

David Pellauer and Bernard Dauenhauer. *(2002) revised
(2020*. Paul Riceour. *Stanford Encyclopedia of Philosophy*.
Retrieved from:
https://plato.stanford.edu/entries/Riceour/

17

Mallett, Oliver and Wapshott, Robert (2011). The challenges of identity work: Developing Riceourian narrative identity in organisations. *ephemera theory & politics in organization.* Retrieved from: https://ephemerajournal.org/sites/default/files/2022-01/11-3mallettwapshott.pdf;

https://ephemerajournal.org/contribution/challenges-identity-work-developing-Riceourian-narrative-identity-organisations#:~:text=Analysing%20the%20organisational%20context%20that,prefiguration%2C%20configuration%20and%20refiguration).

18

Dau, Suzanne (2014). The use of the three-fold mimesis. Academic quarter (akademik), Volume 09. Autumn 2014. Retrieved from: https://www.researchgate.net/publication/270374769_The_use_of_the_three_fold_mimesis

**Refiguration** is the third movement of narrative, the stage in which a story is restored to the real world of action and suffering. It is in the reader that the story reaches its conclusion.

Baker, Joe (2017). Refiguration, Understanding and Transformation. Retrieved from: https://figuration.al/refiguration-understanding-and-transformation-2492d2b40212

19

Turello, D. (2015). How We Experience Time: Paul Riceour on Past, Present, and Future. Retrieved from: https://blogs.loc.gov/kluge/2015/04/paul-Riceour/

20

UK Essays (2022). The Purpose of Phenomenology. Retrieved from: The Purpose of Phenomenology (ukessays.com)

21

Politifact (2017). In Context: Donald Trump's 'very fine people on both sides' remarks (transcript). Retrieved from: PolitiFact | In Context: Donald Trump's 'very fine people on both sides' remarks (transcript)

22

Barnes, Ronald (2016). *Practice What you Preach, Preach What you Practice*. Balboa Press.

23

Vukcevich, Mai (2002). Representation. *University of Chicago*. Retrieved from: https://csmt.uchicago.edu/glossary2004/representation.htm#:~:text=For%20Aristotle%2C%20representation%20becomes%20man's,%2Fsimulacrum%2C%20(2)%5D

24

Greco, Alberto (). THE CONCEPT OF REPRESENTATION IN PSYCHOLOGY. University of Genoa, Italy. Retrieved from: http://cognilab.disfor.unige.it/greco/pubblicazioni/28%20The%20concept%20of%20representation.pdf

25

Cherry, Kendra (2023). How Genes Influence Child Development. *Verywell Mind*. Retrieved from: https://www.verywellmind.com/genes-and-development-2795114#:~:text=Clearly%2C%20genetic%20influences%20have%20an,also%20play%20a%20vital%20role.

---

Thapar, A., & Stergiakouli, E. (2008). Genetic influences on the development of childhood psychiatric disorders. *Psychiatry*, 7(7), 277–281. https://doi.org/10.1016/j.mppsy.2008.05.009. Retrieved from: https://www.ncbi.nlm.nih.gov/pmc/articles/PMC3303131/

26

Firestone, Robert W., (2008). The Human Experience. *Psychology Today*. Retrieved from: https://www.psychologytoday.com/us/blog/the-human-experience/200812/the-human-experience

27

Firestone, Robert W., (2008). The Human Experience. *Psychology Today*. Retrieved from: https://www.psychologytoday.com/us/blog/the-human-experience/200812/the-human-experience

28

Billings, Elsa and Walqui, Alda (1995). Zone of Proximal Development: An Affirmative Perspective in Teaching ELLs. *Wese Ed*. Retrieved from: https://www.wested.org/resources/zone-of-proximal-development/#:~:text=The%20Zone%20of%20Proximal%20Development%20is%20defined%20as%20the%20space, collaboration%20with%20more%20capable%20peers.

Mcleod, Saul, reviewed by Olivia Guy Evans (2023). Vygotsky's Zone Of Proximal Development And Scaffolding. Simply Psychology, Retrieved from: https://www.simplypsychology.org/zone-of-proximal-development.html

Cherry, Kendra (2023). What is Scaffolding in Psychology. Explore Psychology. Retrieved from: https://www.explorepsychology.com/what-is-scaffolding-inpsychology/#:~:text=Scaffolding%20refers%20to%20the%20temporary,trying%20to%20accomplish%20a%20task.

29

Baerheim, Anders and Johanne Ness, Ingunn (2020). Riceour's triple mimesis and the zone of proximal development in the learning processes of inter-professional student teams. *Journal of Pedagogical Sociology and Psychology Volume 2, Issue 2, 2020.* http://www.doi.org/10.33902/JPSP.2020263947. Retrieved from: https://www.jpsp.com/download/Riceours-triple-mimesis-and-the-zone-of-proximal-development-in-the-learning-processes-of-8702.pdf. University of Bergen, Norway.

30

Firestone, Robert W., (2008). The Human Experience. *Psychology Today.* Retrieved from: https://www.psychologytoday.com/us/blog/the-human-experience/200812/the-human-experience

31

World Data. Info (2021). Retrieved from: https://www.worlddata.info/life-expectancy.php#:~:text=The%20world%20average%20age%20of,data%20from%20the%20year%202020.

32

Hofweber, Thomas (2020). "Logic and Ontology". *The Stanford Encyclopedia of Philosophy.* Metaphysics Research Lab, Stanford University. Retrieved from: https://plato.stanford.edu/entries/logic-ontology/

Epstein, Brian (2018). Social Ontology. *The Stanford Encyclopedia of Philosophy.* Metaphysics Research Lab, Stanford University. Retrieved from: https://plato.stanford.edu/entries/social-ontology/

De Haan, Neils (2021). Journal of Social Ontology. Retrieved from: https://www.degruyter.com/journal/key/jso/html

33

Wiebke Bleidorn, Christopher J. Hopwood, Mitja D. Back, Jaap J. A. Denissen, Marie Hennecke, Patrick L. Hill, Markus Jokela, Christian Kandler, Richard E. Lucas, Maike Luhmann, Ulrich Orth, Brent W. Roberts, Jenny Wagner, Cornelia Wrzus, Johannes Zimmermann (2021). *Personality Trait Stability and Change.* Retrieved from: https://ps.psychopen.eu/index.php/ps/article/view/600 9/6009.html#:~:text=In%20summary%2C%20the%20liter ature%20on,and%20potentially%20also%20old%20age. ; https://ps.psychopen.eu/index.php/ps/article/view/600 9/6009.html#:~:text=In%20summary%2C%20the%20liter ature%20on,and%20potentially%20also%20old%20age.

Bleidorn, W., Hopwood, C. J., Back, M. D., Denissen, J. J. A., Hennecke, M., Hill, P. L., Jokela, M., Kandler, C., Lucas, R. E., Luhmann, M., Orth, U., Roberts, B. W., Wagner, J., Wrzus, C., & Zimmermann, J. (2021). Personality Trait Stability and Change. *Personality Science, 2*, 1-20. https://doi.org/10.5964/ps.6009

Mathew A. Harris, Caroline E. Brett, Wendy Johnson and Ian J. Deary (2016). Personality Stability From Age 14 to Age 77 Years. Psychol Aging. 2016 Dec; 31(8): 862–874. doi: 10.1037/pag0000133. PMCID: PMC5144810, PMID: 27929341. Retrieved from:

https://www.ncbi.nlm.nih.gov/pmc/articles/PMC514481
0/#:~:text=Although%20lifelong%20personality%20stabili
ty%20has,across%20the%20entire%20life%20course.

34

Tanasugarn, Annie, PhD (2022). How Childhood
Attachment Trauma Can Affect Adult Relationships.
*Psychology Today*. Retrieved from:
https://www.psychologytoday.com/us/blog/understandi
ng-ptsd/202205/how-childhood-attachment-trauma-can-
affect-adult-relationships

35

Tanasugarn, Annie, PhD (2022). How Childhood
Attachment Trauma Can Affect Adult Relationships.
*Psychology Today*. Retrieved from:
https://www.psychologytoday.com/us/blog/understandi
ng-ptsd/202205/how-childhood-attachment-trauma-can-
affect-adult-relationships

36

Tanasugarn, Annie, PhD (2022). How Childhood
Attachment Trauma Can Affect Adult Relationships.
*Psychology Today*. Retrieved from:
https://www.psychologytoday.com/us/blog/understandi
ng-ptsd/202205/how-childhood-attachment-trauma-can-
affect-adult-relationships

37

Nelson, C. A., Zeanah, C. H. and Fox, N. A. (2019). How
Early Experience Shapes Human Development: The Case
of Psychosocial Deprivation. Neural Plast. 2019; 2019:
1676285. Published online 2019 Jan 15.
doi: 10.1155/2019/1676285. Retrieved from:
https://www.ncbi.nlm.nih.gov/pmc/articles/PMC635053
7/

---

38

Nelson, C. A., Zeanah, C. H. and Fox, N. A. (2019). How Early Experience Shapes Human Development: The Case of Psychosocial Deprivation. Neural Plast. 2019; 2019: 1676285. Published online 2019 Jan 15. doi: 10.1155/2019/1676285. Retrieved from: https://www.ncbi.nlm.nih.gov/pmc/articles/PMC6350537/

39

Cherry, Kendra (2020). Freud's Psychosexual Stages of Development. Medically reviewed by Steven Gans, MD. Retrieved from: https://www.verywellmind.com/freuds-stages-of-psychosexual-development-2795962#:~:text=During%20the%20five%20psychosexual%20stages,the%20driving%20force%20behind%20behavior.

40

Cherry, Kendra (2020). Child Development Theories and Examples. Reviewed by Amy Morin, LCSW. Retrieved from: https://www.verywellmind.com/child-development-theories-2795068

41

Cherry, Kendra (2020) Cherry, Kendra (2019). How Social Learning Theory Works. Reviewed by Amy Morin, LCSW. Retrieved from: https://www.verywellmind.com/social-learning-theory-2795074

42

Bandura, Albert (1991). Social cognitive theory of self-regulation. *Organizational Behavior and Human Decision Processes*, Volume 50, Issue 2, 1991, Pages 248-287, ISSN 0749-5978, https://doi.org/10.1016/0749-5978(91)90022-L .

Retrieved from:
https://www.sciencedirect.com/science/article/pii/0749
59789190022L

43

Cherry, Kendra (2020) Cherry, Kendra (2019). How Social
Learning Theory Works. Reviewed by Amy Morin, LCSW.
Retrieved from: https://www.verywellmind.com/social-
learning-theory-2795074

44

Carey, Michael P., PhD and Forsyth, Andrew D.  (2009).
Teaching Tip Sheet: Self-Efficacy.
American Psychological Association (APA).

Retrieved from:
https://www.apa.org/pi/aids/resources/education/self-
efficacy

45

Cherry, Kendra (2019). Cherry, Kendra (2019). Intrinsic
Motivation. Reviewed by Amy Morin, LCSW. Retrieved
from: https://www.verywellmind.com/what-is-intrinsic-
motivation-2795385

46

Nelson, C. A., Zeanah, C. H. and Fox, N. A. (2019). How
Early Experience Shapes Human Development: The Case
of Psychosocial Deprivation. Neural Plast. 2019; 2019:
1676285. Published online 2019 Jan15.
doi: 10.1155/2019/1676285. Retrieved from:
https://www.ncbi.nlm.nih.gov/pmc/articles/PMC635053
7/

47

Cherry, Kendra (2019). What Is Attachment Theory? Medically reviewed by Steven Gans, MD. Retrieved from: https://www.verywellmind.com/what-is-attachment-theory-2795337

48

Bandura, Albert  (1978). Self-efficacy: Toward a unifying theory of behavioral change. Advances in Behaviour Research and Therapy, Volume 1, Issue 4, 1978, Pages 139-161. https://doi.org/10.1016/0146-6402(78)90002-4. Retrieved from: https://www.sciencedirect.com/science/article/abs/pii/0146640278900024

Cherry, Kendra (2020). Child Development Theories and Examples. Reviewed by Amy Morin, LCSW. Retrieved from: https://www.verywellmind.com/child-development-theories-2795068

49

Bandura, Albert  (1978). Self-efficacy: Toward a unifying theory of behavioral change. Advances in Behaviour Research and Therapy, Volume 1, Issue 4, 1978, Pages 139-161. https://doi.org/10.1016/0146-6402(78)90002-4. Retrieved from: https://www.sciencedirect.com/science/article/abs/pii/0146640278900024

Cherry, Kendra (2020). The Different Types of Attachment Styles. Reviewed by David Susman, PhD. Retrieved from: https://www.verywellmind.com/attachment-styles-2795344

50

Cherry, Kendra (2020). The Different Types of Attachment Styles. Reviewed by David Susman, PhD. Retrieved from: https://www.verywellmind.com/attachment-styles-2795344

51

Cherry, Kendra (2020). The Different Types of Attachment Styles. Reviewed by David Susman, PhD. Retrieved from: https://www.verywellmind.com/attachment-styles-2795344

52

Cherry, Kendra (2020). The Different Types of Attachment Styles. Reviewed by David Susman, PhD. Retrieved from: https://www.verywellmind.com/attachment-styles-2795344

53

Cherry, Kendra (2020). The Different Types of Attachment Styles. Reviewed by David Susman, PhD. Retrieved from: https://www.verywellmind.com/attachment-styles-2795344

54

Cherry, Kendra (2020). The Different Types of Attachment Styles. Reviewed by David Susman, PhD. Retrieved from: https://www.verywellmind.com/attachment-styles-2795344

55

Nelson, C. A., Zeanah, C. H. and Fox, N. A. (2019). How Early Experience Shapes Human Development: The Case of Psychosocial Deprivation. Neural Plast. 2019; 2019: 1676285. Published online 2019 Jan 15. doi: 10.1155/2019/1676285.

Retrieved from:
https://www.ncbi.nlm.nih.gov/pmc/articles/PMC635053
7/

56

Cherry, Kendra (2020). Erik Erikson's Stages of
Psychosocial Development.
Reviewed by David Susman, PhD. Retrieved from:
https://www.verywellmind.com/erik-eriksons-stages-of-
psychosocial-development-2795740

Cherry, Kendra (2020). Psychosocial Development: The 8
Stages We All Go Through According to Erik Erikson.
Retrieved from: https://www.verywellmind.com/what-is-
conflict-2794976

Conflict During the Stages of Psychosocial Development
https://www.verywellmind.com/what-is-conflict-2794976
Orenstein, Gabriel A. and Lewis Lindsay (2020). Eriksons
Stages of Psychosocial Development. *NCBI*. Retrieved
from: https://www.ncbi.nlm.nih.gov/books/NBK556096/

57

Cherry, Kendra (2020). Erik Erikson's Stages of
Psychosocial Development.Reviewed by David Susman,
PhD. Retrieved from:
https://www.verywellmind.com/erik-eriksons-stages-of
psychosocial-development-2795740

Cherry, Kendra (2020). Psychosocial Development: The 8
Stages We All Go Through According to Erik Erikson.
Retrieved from: https://www.verywellmind.com/what-is-
conflict-2794976

Conflict During the Stages of Psychosocial Development. Retrieved from: https://www.verywellmind.com/what-is-conflict-2794976
Orenstein, Gabriel A. and Lewis Lindsay (2020). Eriksons Stages of Psychosocial Development. *NCBI*. Retrieved from: https://www.ncbi.nlm.nih.gov/books/NBK556096/

58

Cherry, Kendra (2020). Erik Erikson's Stages of Psychosocial Development.Reviewed by David Susman, PhD. Retrieved from: https://www.verywellmind.com/erik-eriksons-stages-of-psychosocial-development-2795740

Orenstein, Gabriel A. and Lewis Lindsay (2020). Eriksons Stages of Psychosocial Development. *NCBI*. Retrieved from: https://www.ncbi.nlm.nih.gov/books/NBK556096/

59

Orenstein, Gabriel A. and Lewis Lindsay (2020). Eriksons Stages of Psychosocial Development. *NCBI*. Retrieved from: https://www.ncbi.nlm.nih.gov/books/NBK556096/

60

Cherry, Kendra (2020). Erik Erikson's Stages of Psychosocial Development.Reviewed by David Susman, PhD. Retrieved from: https://www.verywellmind.com/erik-eriksons-stages-of-psychosocial-development-2795740

Orenstein, Gabriel A. and Lewis Lindsay (2020). Eriksons Stages of Psychosocial Development. *NCBI*. Retrieved from: https://www.ncbi.nlm.nih.gov/books/NBK556096/

61

Cherry, Kendra (2020). Erik Erikson's Stages of Psychosocial Development.Reviewed by David Susman, PhD. Retrieved from: https://www.verywellmind.com/erik-eriksons-stages-of-psychosocial-development-2795740

Orenstein, Gabriel A. and Lewis Lindsay (2020). Eriksons Stages of Psychosocial Development. *NCBI*. Retrieved from: https://www.ncbi.nlm.nih.gov/books/NBK556096/

62

Cherry, Kendra (2020). Erik Erikson's Stages of Psychosocial Development.Reviewed by David Susman, PhD. Retrieved from: https://www.verywellmind.com/erik-eriksons-stages-of-psychosocial-development-2795740

Orenstein, Gabriel A. and Lewis Lindsay (2020). Eriksons Stages of Psychosocial Development. *NCBI*. Retrieved from: https://www.ncbi.nlm.nih.gov/books/NBK556096/

63

Cherry, Kendra (2020). Erik Erikson's Stages of Psychosocial Development.Reviewed by David Susman, PhD. Retrieved from: https://www.verywellmind.com/erik-eriksons-stages-of-psychosocial-development-2795740

Orenstein, Gabriel A. and Lewis Lindsay (2020). Eriksons Stages of Psychosocial Development. *NCBI*. Retrieved from: https://www.ncbi.nlm.nih.gov/books/NBK556096/

64

Cherry, Kendra (2020). Erik Erikson's Stages of
Psychosocial Development.
Reviewed by David Susman, PhD. Retrieved from:
https://www.verywellmind.com/erik-eriksons-stages-of-
psychosocial-development-2795740
Orenstein, Gabriel A. and Lewis Lindsay (2020). Eriksons
Stages of Psychosocial Development. *NCBI*. Retrieved
from: https://www.ncbi.nlm.nih.gov/books/NBK556096/

65

Cherry, Kendra (2020). Erik Erikson's Stages of
Psychosocial Development.Reviewed by David Susman,
PhD. Retrieved from:
https://www.verywellmind.com/erik-eriksons-stages-of-
psychosocial-development-2795740
Orenstein, Gabriel A. and Lewis Lindsay (2020). Eriksons
Stages of Psychosocial Development. *NCBI*. Retrieved
from: https://www.ncbi.nlm.nih.gov/books/NBK556096/

66

Cherry, Kendra (2020). Child Development Theories and
Examples. Reviewed by Amy Morin, LCSW. Retrieved
from: https://www.verywellmind.com/child-development-
theories-2795068

67

Cherry, Kendra (2020). The 4 Stages of Cognitive
Development.  Medically reviewed by Steven Gans, MD.
Retrieved from: https://www.verywellmind.com/piagets-
stages-of-cognitive-development-2795457

68

Cherry, Kendra (2020). The 4 Stages of Cognitive Development.  Medically reviewed by Steven Gans, MD. Retrieved from: https://www.verywellmind.com/piagets-stages-of-cognitive-development-2795457

69

Cherry, Kendra (2020). The 4 Stages of Cognitive Development.  Medically reviewed by Steven Gans, MD. Retrieved from: https://www.verywellmind.com/piagets-stages-of-cognitive-development-2795457

70

Cherry, Kendra (2020). The 4 Stages of Cognitive Development.  Medically reviewed by Steven Gans, MD. Retrieved from: https://www.verywellmind.com/piagets-stages-of-cognitive-development-2795457

71

Esteban-guitart M. The biosocial foundation of the early Vygotsky: Educational psychology before the zone of proximal development. Hist Psychol. 2018;21(4):384-401. doi:10.1037/hop0000092

Kendra Cherry (2022).  Medically reviewed by Amy Morin, LCSW. What Is Sociocultural Theory? *Verywell Mind.* https://www.verywellmind.com/what-is-sociocultural-theory-2795088

72

Esteban-guitart M. The biosocial foundation of the early Vygotsky: Educational psychology before the zone of proximal development. Hist Psychol. 2018;21(4):384-401. doi:10.1037/hop0000092

Kendra Cherry (2022). Medically reviewed by Amy Morin, LCSW. What Is Sociocultural Theory? *Verywell Mind.* https://www.verywellmind.com/what-is-sociocultural-theory-2795088

73

Esteban-guitart M. The biosocial foundation of the early Vygotsky: Educational psychology before the zone of proximal development. Hist Psychol. 2018;21(4):384-401. doi:10.1037/hop0000092

Kendra Cherry (2022). Medically reviewed by Amy Morin, LCSW. What Is Sociocultural Theory? *Verywell Mind.* https://www.verywellmind.com/what-is-sociocultural-theory-2795088

74

Kendra Cherry (2022). Medically reviewed by Amy Morin, LCSW. What Is Sociocultural Theory? *Verywell Mind.* https://www.verywellmind.com/what-is-sociocultural-theory-2795088

75

Kendra Cherry (2022). Medically reviewed by Amy Morin, LCSW. What Is Sociocultural Theory? *Verywell Mind.* https://www.verywellmind.com/what-is-sociocultural-theory-2795088

NYSED Office of Bilingual Education and World Language. The zone of proximal development: An affirmative perspective in teaching ELLs/MLLs.

76

GONGALA, SAGARI. MEDICALLY REVIEWED BY DR. NEHA BHAVE SALANKAR (2023). What Is Social Referencing In A Child's Development? Referenced from: https://www.momjunction.com/articles/what-is-social-referencing-in-child-development_00356657/

Social Referencing – A Complete Explanation. Retrieved from: https://www.mffy.com/blog/social-referencing-a-complete-explanation

77

GONGALA, SAGARI. MEDICALLY REVIEWED BY DR. NEHA BHAVE SALANKAR (2023). What Is Social Referencing In A Child's Development? Referenced from: https://www.momjunction.com/articles/what-is-social-referencing-in-child-development_00356657/

78

Social Referencing – A Complete Definition. Retrieved from: https://dictionary.apa.org/social-referencing

Erstad, W. (2023). What is Social Referencing in Child Development? An Easy Explanation. Rasmussen University. https://www.rasmussen.edu/degrees/education/blog/what-is-social-referencing-in-child-development/#:~:text=Social%20referencing%20is%20defined%20by,as%20the%20child%20gets%20older.

79

Huxley, Elizabeth; Seaton, Daisy; Grenyer, Brin (2021). Remembered childhood invalidation as a predictor of narcissism, personality functioning, and wellbeing. Personality and Individual Differences, Science Direct.

Retrieved from:
https://reader.elsevier.com/reader/sd/pii/S01918869210
00611?token=DE87F7507409597C845F04E273479D8BD0
FB3C5B5E918D81FB19D43FF27B6E1E28DE4E1B71D45B
2A78321790AAF518CD&originRegion=us-east-
1&originCreation=20230228163057

80

Tanasugarn, Annie (2022). Childhood Invalidation Can
Affect Adult Well-Being. Psychology Today. Retrieved
from:
https://www.psychologytoday.com/us/blog/understandi
ng-ptsd/202207/childhood-invalidation-can-affect-adult-
well-being

81

Tanasugarn, Annie (2022). Childhood Invalidation Can
Affect Adult Well-Being. Psychology Today. Retrieved
from:
https://www.psychologytoday.com/us/blog/understandi
ng-ptsd/202207/childhood-invalidation-can-affect-adult-
well-being

82

Borba, Michele (2022). Child psychologist: The No. 1 skill
that sets mentally strong kids apart from 'those who give
up'—and how parents can teach it. Retrieved from:
https://www.cnbc.com/2022/07/04/psychologist-shares-
the-top-skill-that-sets-mentally-strong-kids-from-those-
who-give-up-easily.html

83

Koehler, Jessica (2023). , Achieving an Equilibrium of the
Mind. Psychology Today. Retrieved from:
https://www.psychologytoday.com/ie/blog/beyond-
school-walls/202306/achieving-an-equilibrium-of-the-
mind

---

Bennett, K., & Dorjee, D. (2016). The impact of a mindfulness-based stress reduction course (MBSR) on well-being and academic attainment of sixth-form students. *Mindfulness, 7*(1), 105–114. https://doi.org/10.1007/s12671-015-0430-7 Retrieved from: https://psycnet.apa.org/record/2015-34484-001

Sutcliffe, K. M., Vogus, T. J., & Dane, E. (2016). Mindfulness in organizations: A cross-level review. *Annual Review of Organizational Psychology and Organizational Behavior, 3,* 55–81. https://doi.org/10.1146/annurev-orgpsych-041015-062531 . Retrieved from: https://psycnet.apa.org/record/2016-34486-003

Costa, P. T., & McCrae, R. R. (1992). The five-factor model of personality and its relevance to personality disorders. *Journal of Personality Disorders, 6*(4), 343–359. https://doi.org/10.1521/pedi.1992.6.4.343 . Retrieved from: https://psycnet.apa.org/record/1993-33707-001

Khan Academy. Big five personality traits and health behaviors. Retrieved from: https://www.khanacademy.org/test-prep/mcat/social-sciences-practice/social-science-practice-tut/e/big-five-personality-traits-and-health-behaviors

www.ingramcontent.com/pod-product-compliance
Lightning Source LLC
Chambersburg PA
CBHW071159300726
48975CB00004B/1218